ROSIE IN RACHEL

ROSIE IN RACHEL

ROSIE LOGAN

BLOOMSBURY

First published 1992
Copyright © 1992 by Rosie Logan

The moral right of the author
has been asserted

Bloomsbury Publishing Ltd,
2 Soho Square, London W1V 5DE

A CIP catalogue record for this book
is available from the British Library

ISBN 0 7475 1115 2

10 9 8 7 6 5 4 3 2 1

Typeset in Great Britain by
Hewer Text Composition Services, Edinburgh
Printed in Great Britain by
Butler and Tanner Ltd, Frome and London

CHAPTER ONE

'Good-night son.'

I stroked Mark's limp, silky hair as he sat peacefully sprawled out on a soft-back sofa, his wise yet somehow innocent eyes glued to the television. What he was so engrossed in I was unaware of, for I had by this time completely lost my sense of concentration, as if some cruel, unknown force had deliberately set out to destroy the zest and enthusiasm I'd had for living, as if I was dead. The only control left within my brain was over my thinning legs, so as to walk from one necessary place to another, moving towards the toilet to tip urine from my bladder, then putting the kettle on to make one of the endless cups of coffee or tea in order to fill once again my bladder.

The colour of Mark's fifteen-year-old head changed from brown to beigy-pink, so I knew he had tilted his face towards mine. When I think back, how my dead features must have bewildered him, since, not long before, a matter of months past, Mark would brag to his rowdy friends how beautiful and clever his enthusiastic mother was.

'Good-night, Mum. God bless.'

I shuddered as I stared into his blood-stained face, great ugly streaks running straight across his once delicate profile. The blood vessels behind my eyes were constantly haemorrhaging – though in my near-blind state, the blood would clot thus causing a huge bizarre brown spider to stick on every living thing I gazed at.

I knelt beside Mark kissing his rough, boyish hands – within my tired heart I knew I should have begged forgiveness for the cunning, selfish thought that was stirring inside my hungry brain, but I didn't.

I put on one of my holy smiles and whispered, 'Always remember, Mark, I love you, no matter what other people say . . . I love you.'

I clutched the tiny, brown plastic bottle concealed in the pocket of my cheap orange nylon dressing-gown, turned and began dragging my aching body up the flight of stairs which was covered in tatty, sponge-backed carpet. My feet were bare and I felt the ragged holes beneath my steps. My distorted mind wandered back to the time the carpet was first laid – how happy I was, with my painted mouth full of tiny nails, laying the first tap, banging away with the hammer, saying to myself, Fuck the neighbours if they complain about the continuous thump-thumping, because today I am laying the first step towards happiness. With my new council house comes our new life. From now on everything will be rosy.

To be completely free was my goal in life, not realising just how lonely freedom could be. I had freed myself from the tight chains of religion, making my mind strong enough to decide which was God and which was evil, without any superstitious authority manipulating my brain. I had also jumped away from the self-indulgent group into which I was born, thinking myself strong enough to place time, instead of money, top of my loving list. It terrified me to think that to achieve total freedom from society and all its complicated rules and regulations was to achieve the horror of mental isolation which, I began to think, only the insane could endure. Still, I kidded myself I could enjoy my designed freedom, that is, until blindness threatened my beautiful, planned happiness. Mental isolation I could almost accept, but walking hand in hand with a visual loneliness . . . the two became a deadly-cruel killer.

To fight for political freedom is to be called a revolutionary, or suffragette. To shed the chains of royal pomp is eccentric, but if you are poor and wish to free yourself from society, then you are labelled insane.

Once, on a beautiful, hot, sultry summer's day, after spending the early part of the day bustling round my house with no shoes on my feet, I thought I might as well clean the windows. It was one of the rare days when I was blessed with an overspill of energy. So, without sticking to the rules of convention, I walked as gay as spring to a local shop to purchase a bottle of Windolene. I hadn't bothered to trap my happy toes into a piece of uncomfortable leather.

Half-way to the shop two loud-mouthed youths passed by, and jeeringly remarked, 'Look at that mad woman. What a lunatic.'

Thus to be free from the hold of society is to be insane . . .

'Mum, tell Mark to turn down the telly,' yelled my thirteen-year-old daughter, who had half an hour earlier retired to bed.

I groaned her request back to Mark. Within seconds the harsh blare from the TV became no more than a delicate whisper as I entered Sarah's squashed-up bedroom, for she occupied the smallest of the three, which was about four times larger than a dog kennel. With my foggy, bloodstained eyes I gazed at Sarah more through memory than sight. Her round, pink face was full of innocence, with wide-apart, sensitive blue eyes, unlike those of a hunter, set near to each other, making it easier for the hunter to seek out his prey. Sarah's eyes were that of the deer who was always on the run, looking behind for fear of being attacked by the lion or wolf.

'You feel all right, Mum?' pleaded Sarah, as she gently squeezed my hand.

'I'm OK, babe,' said I, returning the squeeze. A huge lump sprang from my heart into my throat – Mum, she called me. What a title to give one as self-pitying as I, too good for the likes of me. Both these young human beings left for my guidance, I felt sick at the thought of it. 'You know how much I love you, Sarah,' said I, kissing the tip of her small cold nose. 'Never forget how much I love you . . .'

Ten minutes later I was sitting upright in bed with a glass of water and twenty-four sleeping pills.

'I'm already dead inside, it's now just a matter of killing the outer case, which is my body. What a pisshole of a world,' mumbled I, slipping the first tablet into my eager lips. I rested my head back into the mock-feather pillow, I dug my head into the foam. 'Even the fucking pillows I rest on are imitation.' I pushed another tablet into my mouth . . . false hair, plastic tits, rubber flowers, false values, where will it all end up? In a bloody nut house, that's where. I was getting angry

again. 'Calm down, Rosie,' I told myself . . .
in went another pill.

Now let me think, when did I first start
being a neurotic? Was it after the tall, faceless man in the park? No! No! I thought: I'll
push that grim memory back into the cobweb
corners of my infant life.

The sudden scream of a garden cat made
my neck throb with fear. I put my hands round
my neck and felt the heavy beat each side of
my windpipe.

No, not tonight, cat, you'll not take my
sleep from me. Was it last night or the
night before when you, ugly beast as huge
as a man, clawed and pounded on my back
door, terrifying my whole being . . . ? Tonight
I sleep.

Two pills, one after the other, jumped
into my mouth. I began to feel beautifully
peaceful.

Perhaps it all began when I was nine
years old, when my beloved father lay ice-
cold in a dark, shining coffin, a blue willow
saucer placed beneath his icy tomb, with
two half-onions to counteract the smell of
dead flesh.

I wonder what they use today in order to smother the stench of the dead, I asked myself, and immediately gave the answer. Something all scientific, I suppose, all clean, clinical and smooth tucked away under the carpet, just like the great flood of nervous disorders that are all around me. For each side of my house, every housewife I know, in fact the whole street, people, kids, dogs, every bloody one of them on some kind of pill or sedative. You can't put facts down to my tormented brain playing tricks on me . . . Oh . . . Balls to the world . . . balls . . . balls . . . balls.

I was dead to the world, and it had taken me two long, lonely weeks of secret cunning plots to achieve my suicide. I felt just like a convict longing for the day of his release. For more weeks than I could remember, I had been trapped in my house like a caged beast, except that my feelings were far worse because the iron bars were self-made. The great world outside was ready and waiting, just one step across my own front door . . . if only I could conjure up the dormant courage rotting away within my dead heart.

Many months before, I had tried to cope with my loss of sight by trying to carry on exactly as before. I continued to visit different public houses with my trendy friends I had happily acquired over the years. They were all married women, and mostly of my own age-group. All except two were on anti-depressant pills so as to kill the everyday monotony of living. We decided to take one night out each week to forget our ever-growing problems at home, and it all seemed to work splendidly for my friends. They laughed, drank, and danced while I, like a brandy-soaked cabbage, sat sadly at the bar listening to the great happiness, the constant giggling and chattering. And each week it got worse and worse, I just got more and more lost with every Friday-night knees-up with the girls.

I tormented myself with one burning question: How can I, surrounded by so many, be so pitifully lonely?

A few times, different men would give an instantly cruel remark as my friend Joan and I walked into a public house holding hands. Joan tried her best to guide me carefully through the throbbing crowd, without drawing too much attention to my blindness.

'Here comes a pair of lesbians,' then a burst of mocking laughter, and on each occasion I crumbled.

I wanted to scream, Pisshole world: Why must men assume bad intentions behind any act of love or caring for another human being . . . Even my daughter's love was misinterpreted by men, for she heard the phrase, 'Your mother's drunk' far too often when she reached out to stop me falling from the platform of a bus when stepping off.

Because of the constant attacks on my morality, it didn't take long for me to become a hermit. I had completely turned away from society and its lack of understanding. I wondered how many had suffered before I . . . the blind, the deaf and the crippled. My sense of compassion for those lost in history became so intense, it was as if to me the world was made up of selfish, greedy beings, except for those who suffered mental and physical hurt. I thought myself honoured to be part of such a beautiful company . . . So fuck the rest of the world, let them tear each other apart, for I am no longer in the game.

My mind was firmly set on suicide. I was completely convinced that nothing on earth could cure the constant aching.

It was a Tuesday morning when I phoned the family doctor and asked for a prescription to be made out for my husband Jim, who I had ten months earlier been separated from. I convinced the doctor that Jim was being kept awake at night because of the unbearable pains brought on by his ulcer. I suggested that some heavy sleepers might help my husband, or at least that they might give him a full night's rest. The doctor agreed, and wrote out the prescription.

How do I get to the surgery? I asked myself, because at this point I was paranoid with fear at the thought of entering the street.

So I asked my home help Anne, issued to me by our local social services department, to go. I told unsuspecting Anne that the pills were no more than a tonic to help me regain a little of the one and a half stone I had so rapidly lost.

*

Each Wednesday, since my ill health, my loyal mother had visited my home carrying her thick brown leather shopping bag full to the zip-brim with goodies: a pound of sausages, a few bananas for the kids, a box of tea bags or a few bacon rashers she had left over from her sensible larder. Each Wednesday was like Christmas when Mum gave us her presents. At the age of seventy, she was as lively as a thirty year old. She was round and unbelievably soft on the surface – always pink, her skin. This was maybe because she never had a holiday away from home until she was in her late-sixties. I suppose if any woman had been shut up in factories all her natural life, away from the sunshine, she must inevitably turn out pink, not white, because factories made you warm and sweaty . . . and so did a great heavy wringer on wash days, and so did a giant stone copper heated underneath by a roaring fire.

The steam would bellow out into Mum's face making her seem like a poor boiled lobster that was never really done, just tormented with steam all its long pink days. Now and then, under heavy pressure, just like a lobster, she would spitefully nip you when it was least expected.

Her blows were so heavy and quick, like a sting, they left you shocked and dazed, and sometimes scared . . . Then, as age crept up on Mother, her strength dwindled with each grey hair. And Mum, so used to attacking, had to arm herself from another reliable source. She discovered what a quick weapon her agile tongue could be. Like a razor, it cut into my soul mightier than any fist, but I loved her for her strong sense of survival: strike and get in first before they have the chance to attack you. A widow at forty, left with five, freedom-loving children to bring up as respectably as humanly possible, in such poverty and loneliness, must have been like a nightmare, so Mum could never find time for love and understanding. I think if she had found the time to really look at her offspring, and seen beneath the surface of it all, she would have cracked under the flood of sorrow all around her.

'You just get up, you lazy mare.' Mum's granite voice echoed round the kitchen.

I stared at her short, dark shadow – she

raised her heavy, laden holdall and plonked it on to the table, making my empty cup and saucer dance with fright. Penny and Blossom, my two mongrel dogs, scampered under my chair for protection, their trembling, tiny bodies pressed against my right calf.

'You frightened the dogs – '

She never waited for me to finish the sentence. As always, Mum interrupted.

'Bloody things, you ought to have them put to sleep.' Without looking in my direction, Mum began unloading the contents of her bag on to the table. 'You can't afford to feed yourself, let alone bloody dogs.'

I wanted to scream, Mum, look at me, I am nothing but bone and boils, and I am going to die next Wednesday, but the words would not leave my throat. I could ask Mum to help me, if only she could see it in my eyes, in my lazy, useless way of living. My eyes pleaded: Please, Mum, help me. Mum, I am lost.

Mum took no notice of my sad appearance, for she was also blind but in a far different way to me. Some can look at a Christmas tree and never notice that it's real, not plastic –

the dazzle of the tinsel and coloured lights is so strong, it smothers the beauty of the living tree.

Mother, I love you with all my being, why are we on such different wavelengths? What a freak of nature I am, for if I can't communicate with my own mother, what's to become of me?

After an hour of Mum chatting about things of little importance, she left me alone once again with my distorted thoughts of life and all its mysteries.

When a soul is losing her sight, how does she cope? How does she prepare for the tragic event that will change her whole way of life – knowing that soon there will never be another sunset of red, gold and grey lying at the end of the garden, to warm her heart and brush away, as if by magic, the problems of the day. Never again to witness the growth of a wonderful, giant sunflower standing like a plant from another world. A tiny seed, swept around our planet for a million years, before finding the right place in which to sink its roots.

CHAPTER TWO

Exactly one week later I was in a world of unconsciousness. As planned, I had taken the overdose on Tuesday night, making sure that my mother would find me the next morning, being as she always as regular as clockwork paid a visit to my home. I didn't want Mark and Sarah to cope with the tragic situation.

At eleven o'clock mid-morning, Sarah entered my room, still dreamy-eyed from her late lie-in.

'Mum, Mum, wake up, it's eleven o'clock.' She shook me gently. I gave no response so she shook my shoulder hard and repeated, 'Mum, Mum, wake up.'

As if dead, I lay there motionless. A tinge of panic flickered in her puzzled eyes. She screamed with fear to her brother lying half-asleep in the next bedroom.

'Mark, Mark, I can't wake Mummy, she's freezing cold like she is dead.'

Mark immediately leapt from his warm bed, stunned and shaken by Sarah's panic-stricken voice. He touched my forehead like an inexperienced student of medicine about to witness his first operation, pretending to be in full control of the situation, yet afraid of his reaction to his first glimpse of reality. Within minutes, Mark reassured his weeping sister.

'It's all right, Sarah, Mummy's in a diabetic coma.'

My family had coped many times before with my comatose body. After twenty-two years of daily insulin, I was first-class at causing panic and confusion. How many times I had been rushed off to hospital because of ill health was impossible to remember.

'Quick, Sarah, run downstairs and phone Nannie,' ordered Mark with an air of great manliness.

My mother acted in her usual responsible way. Without causing any chaos she told

Sarah to run across the road and tell the doctor. Sarah obeyed with robot-like obedience.

'Doctor,' she sobbed, 'Mummy's in a coma and we can't wake her up, please come and look at her.'

Ten minutes later the doctor arrived. 'Now then, what's the problem?' smiled the calm man in a well-rehearsed voice.

Sarah gave no reply as she pointed upstairs, her throat choked to bursting-point with tears.

'What's wrong with our Mum?' begged Mark.

The doctor leaned over my face and prised open my limp eyelids. Penny and Blossom sat policing him should he make a wrong move, their small black eyes giving off warning signals.

'Mark, Mark,' shouted Mother, slamming the street door behind her, 'where's your mother?'

Mark answered, 'Upstairs, Nan.'

Mum rushed upstairs with elephant footsteps.

'What's going on here?' demanded Mother. 'Are you the doctor?'

The doctor spun round in surprise at mother's forceful, angry attitude, unaware of the fact that my mother could create conflict between a Christian and a cucumber, let alone between herself and a doctor dealing with a death. After a few heated words a decision was reached between the two strong personalities, and it was the doctor who won the position of command, for Mum had to back down under his superior knowledge of medicine.

An ambulance was called and Mark accompanied my body in a ride to the unknown. I had lost control of my brain, so my bladder had been reacting with complete freedom, emptying itself at any embarrassing moment.

'Your mother's pissed her bed,' growled Mum, throwing the blanket off with temper.

Sarah watched her, still in a state of shock, unable to speak.

'What's this?' asked Mum, producing an empty brown plastic bottle from beneath my pillow.

'She's took an overdose.'

Mum phoned the doctor and informed him of her highly important discovery, and the hospital was immediately made aware of his altered diagnosis. Poor, poor Mark, who was also a diabetic, and had been since he was seven years old, his thin legs ravaged by two hypodermic needles forced twice daily into his young tender skin. The local hospital could not deal with my complications, so they transferred me by ambulance to a special poison unit at Romford. Mark, shattered by the reality that his mother might not live, was given his bus fare home by the lady almoner.

When he got there, he exploded with bottled-up tears and wept to his grandmother a statement that was to haunt me for the rest of my days.

'I hate her, I hope she dies. She tried to run away from us for good. I'll never forgive her for as long as I live.'

Suicide is far too easy for those who commit it, they leave behind their selfishness, a debris of mutilated minds, inflicted upon the innocent.

By some strange act of fate, my estranged husband decided to honour me with his presence on the same evening. He arrived at my house to find it desolate and empty except for Penny and Blossom, who, as much as they tried by barking and wagging their tails, could not relate the message of disaster that had struck their comfortable dwelling place.

'Rose, Rose,' called Jim, treading lightly up the stairs, half-expecting to find me in my usual place of the past two months. I had sat alone in my dark bedroom, rocking my tired frame, neither thinking nor crying. On seeing my pathetic position, he would go into a rage and shout, making me jump from my skin, 'You still fucking sulking? Bollocks – I'm going to get drunk,' knowing his threat of drunkenness would deliver my soul into a state of sheer terror.

Finding me not at home filled his mind with uneasy apprehension, especially as of late I had been paranoid about the outside world.

Jim thought I might have been at my mother's, so he phoned her, hoping to confirm that his thoughts of disaster were unnecessary . . . 'Hello, Mum, is Rosie there?'

Mum gobbled up the chance to give Jim the full blast of her tongue, for her fury towards

him had been lying inside her simmering
and brooding like a hot spring, and at that
very moment it was ready to erupt and come
gushing out into a frenzy of hot, boiling
fury. Mum yelled into the phone, spraying
the mouthpiece with sudden spit.

'You bastard! She's taken an overdose.'

Jim winced at the earphone.

'Oh no! What did she have to go and do
a thing like that for?'

Mum was astounded at his reply.

'Do what!' she yelled. 'Because you led
her to it. How many times have I come over
there to find her with a busted mouth or a
black eye?'

Jim interrupted, 'Oh, don't have a go at
me, Mum, just tell me where Rosie is, and
the kids.'

Mum composed herself and explained that
I was in Old Church Hospital at Romford, and
she would be taking care of the children.

When Jim arrived it was just gone eleven
o'clock at night, and I had not yet regained
consciousness. He stayed there till late
Thursday morning and I had still not woken.
He left to have something to eat and a quick

shave, although the nurses had been more than generous with cups of coffee and tea. On his return his heart sank into his suede desert boots, for he found it might be impossible to wake me, ever. The agonising weight of his conscience was unbearable, it was all he could do to hold himself from weeping, which would have damaged his reputation for being an extremely hard man who under no circumstances could break down and show his true emotional feelings.

All through our partnership I wanted to love, and Jim just didn't have the right kind of equipment to satisfy my thirst – sexually, yes, in fact, some might say it was perfect, for he fancied me constantly, twenty-four hours a day, but there was a great amount of confusion because of our different attitudes towards love and sex. My philosophy was that sex was too easy to find compared with real love. I mean to say that if I stopped men in the street, and asked them if they would come home and have sex with me, eight times out of ten I would come up with a result. But if I asked would they come home and love and care for me, I would be bound to draw a blank.

In the early hours of Friday morning I opened my eyes. It was light, electric light . . . I am dead . . . did I succeed and have I been reincarnated with the living . . . ? I wonder what year it is . . .

'Rose, Rose, you all right? It's me, Jim.'

Oh no! Don't say I've failed. 'What do you want?' groaned I with slurry speech. I suddenly realised I was still here, I sprung up in bed like a Jack-in-a-box. 'Oh, my fucking back,' yelled I with temper.

Jim slid his large hands through the bars of my safety cot-bed, and began gently rubbing my aching back . . .

'You feel OK?' sighed Jim with relief.

'What's today?' snapped I.

'It's late Thursday night,' replied Jim with a voice I could not easily recognise, it was soft and trembling with compassion.

I couldn't seem to keep my eyelids open.

'Sorry, Jim, I've got to go to sleep now, see you later.'

I slept for another few hours until an unfamiliar Irish voice awakened me with, 'Mrs Logan, Mrs Logan, how do you feel?'

'Lovely,' smiled I. 'I've been floating.'

Something was hurting my arm, as the woman fiddled and fussed about me.

'What you doing?' I asked sharply.

'Just making sure your drip's OK,' replied the nurse.

'Who are you?' I wanted to know. What kind of humane bastard was trying so desperately to make me live?

'I'm Staff Nurse for tonight,' she told me, proud to announce her position. 'I'm standing in for Sister, Mrs Logan.'

I had never before felt so angry and cheated, deprived of my own death. What bloody downright cheek – I decided to knock her off her pedestal. My voice sounded slurred and stupid, but I wanted it to sound strong and angry; I blabbered on at the staff nurse . . .

'Who gave you permission to interfere with my life? Who do you think you are, God or something? This is me, and if I want to die then mind your own fucking business. Balls to you do-gooders!'

Her footsteps echoed with disgust and she rapidly gave retreat. Two other less important nurses came to my bedside, hovering about my person with dedicated enthusiasm – one, a timid, dark-skinned girl, began combing my long sweaty black hair, her touch was so lovingly gentle, it soothed my angry attitude.

'You have beautiful hair, Rosie, it's as black as a raven's wing.'

At that moment she was all the medicine I needed. To come across someone who really does care . . . I often wonder if my timid, dark friend did really exist, or was she an angel of mercy who only appears when you're at your lowest ebb? Someone to help you through a dark, long night when you feel so helpless and lost.

She gave me a cigarette and held it for me because I was so weak. She prepared a cup of welcome tea when I hadn't eaten or drunk for three days. The gentle nurse gave even more comfort in my lost confidence by telling me how long and lovely my dark eyelashes were. It may have been two or three hours of her precious time she gave me, but I never heard of her existence again for she disappeared with the night.

The dawn crept into the ward bringing with her the sadness of a new grey November day.

My eyes were brighter than they had been for months: what were once ghostly silhouettes were now half-recognisable people, and when they stood real close to me, I could actually see their features. I wondered if my resting perfectly still for so long was the reason for my sudden clearer vision. I was only half happy with the facts, because I was sadly afraid my eyes would soon return back to their natural bloodstained foggy state. The ward I was lying in was huge, long and ugly cold. Most patients, if not all, were suicidal. The whole place echoed with tormented voices, some faint, some strong, some old and some very young, but all with the same sentence ringing through the busy nurses' ears . . . *Leave me alone. Let me die.* Many were unconscious, away from their counterparts, but everyone was pleading for the chance to get out of the rat-race.

A plump little woman in her early sixties waddled over to me.

'You all right now, dear?' she asked with sincerity.

I nodded, 'Yes, thanks, love.'

'You take an overdose, did you?'

I hung my head, ashamed of my failure, and nodded yes.

Her fat stubby fingers clutched mine as she spoke.

'I did too, dear. Didn't work, though. I wish it had. Still, we can't have everything, can we?'

She was so frank and down-to-earth I could hardly believe my own eardrums. The little lady carried on talking about the right way to plan your own death with as much distress as if she were discussing Sunday dinner with her next-door neighbour.

'Won't let you go, will they, the nosy bastards?' sighed she, tucking a straggly strand of her grey hair back behind her ear.

In the half-hour or so that we chatted she told me she was a widow living in an isolated high-rise flat. Her daughter was married and had moved away from London, and visited her mother once or twice a year. The woman poured out her feelings to me, confessing that she was terrified of being lonely.

'I am just not strong enough to cope with loneliness,' she sighed with tear-filled eyes.

'Mrs Logan!' A stern, upright sister interrupted our compassionate conversation. 'Doctor would like a word with you.'

He gave me about three short minutes of his time, enough to say I could leave the hospital that evening. I was still full of drugs and unsteady on my feet. I thought it strange to be discharged so soon, but I was glad of the news that I was going home, for the ward was depressing me more after meeting the sad little woman. I felt an urge to write about her but the feeling did not stay with me for long.

CHAPTER THREE

Home to me was a place of frustration and fear, a place where I was continually burning my hands on my unfriendly electric cooker. My left index-finger was throbbing with pain, as I was forever scalding it as I tried to make a cup of tea. I would hang my finger just inside the cup, then pour in the boiling water until I felt it burn me. Well, at least this stupid method prevented my scalding Penny and Blossom who were around my feet most of the day. Mother said I should try counting until I thought the cup was full, but her bright idea proved unsuccessful, because I misjudged and spilt the boiling water all over Penny's head, making her scream with pain and leaving me full of guilt. The surface of my shin bone was bruised and lumpy, for

Mark and Sarah were unsympathetic to help-lessness. Mark would leave scattered stumbling blocks across the garden path, such as wire and pieces of timber, in readiness to saw and make into new nesting boxes for his treasured pigeons. Once he thoughtlessly placed a heavy toolbox on the back step, and as I opened the garden door to hang out the washing I tripped and fell full-blast into a short, three-foot-high, rough brick wall, tearing my wrist open and banging my head. I sat, in full view of the neighbours, weeping like a child, wanting someone to pick me up and kiss me all better.

Mark shouted, unable to cope with the sight of his pathetic mother, 'Get up! You look like an idiot. Everyone's laughing at you.'

I wanted to scream, Why can't you understand? Ain't there anyone in this poxy world who can know how I am dying inside in so many ways? Mark was rubbing salt into my open wound, and it stung my soul with torment. Months and months of unexplained hurt.

'Mum,' Mark would smile, 'look at my new young bird. Ain't he smashing?'

And I pretended I could see. I would peer through the thin white bars of his shed, forcing my lips into an upward curve, saying, 'Oh Mark, he's beautiful.'

Mark would pull violently away from my side, snapping fast and spiteful, 'You don't care about my pigeon, you ain't even looking at him.'

Immediately I would realise I was looking in the wrong direction, for the inside of Mark's bird loft was dim and my eyes tired. Even with constant squinting, I just couldn't register.

Sick of trying to explain, I would beg Mark, 'I can't see,' but he would never let me finish.

'Oh no, not your bleeding eyes again, go and get yourself a pair of glasses then.'

And off Mark would go, like someone over-sensitive who puts his hands over his eyes, trying to hide away from a sad terrible happening on television. Sarah was just like her brother, she also pretended I wasn't losing my sight.

I felt like a clumsy stumbling giant, groping and groaning around in a cruel world of elegant midgets. My painful hands seemed enormous and ugly, and my bulky feet belonged to a crying fool. Even a spot on my chin became as large as a great throbbing red growth. I began to feel ashamed of my own presence. Food was my worst enemy, for at mealtimes I was mocked for my undisciplined eating habits. Like an infant, I sat with a spoon, pushing a gooey substance on to the stupid utensil with my gravy-stained fingers.

I was totally untrained to cope with my growing disability, and I never had the common sense to complain, proud of the fact that for over twenty years of illness my friends and family had commented on how noble I was in never complaining. I wanted to tell someone that I wasn't strong, and that beneath my smiling canopy of martyrdom there stood a liar and a fake who was afraid of the truth. Being a martyr was splendid for those who suffered on their own, but when this act of noble righteousness affected the loved ones around the ego trip, then this behaviour was surely no more than self-indulgence.

Help – please – somebody help!

*

It was Monday morning, and November was hanging on to the world as if by her depressed fingertips – always a nasty month to me, for at this time of year my head would be heavy with worry and anxiety about how to provide expensive delights for my family at Christmas. How I dreaded the thought of being under obligation to another human being. My squashed little house was situated in a modern cul-de-sac wearing the soppy white-and-black nameplate of Kerry Close – a more apt title would be Crazy Close. To the back and front of my home and spreading all around the left of it stood massive high-rise dwellings poking at the heavy dark sky like a regiment of stone-grey fingers pointed upwards for victory: the deterrent to beat all deterrents of the past.

I opened my front door and its groan made me jump with fright. I stooped and felt round the high concrete step, then I clutched the two bottles of gold-topped milk.

As I straightened my posture my eyes lingered on the great ugly building standing on guard in front of my imagination; I leapt forward fifty years and I was standing in the dock inside a splendid new courtroom full of white-wigged faces and black-cloaked bodies, but I could see the skeleton features of the Judge sitting in a tall polished chair way up, nearly to the great white ceiling. He stared over his dark, thick-rimmed spectacles, looking down on me as if I were a frightened maggot that had just crawled from the skirting board.

The Judge cleared his throat with the precision of all men at the Bar throughout English history.

'Mrs Pogan,' he bellowed.

'Logan, sir,' whispered I.

He replied after yet another throat-clearing exercise, 'Yes, yes, speak up, Mrs Pogan.'

I shook my head slowly, indicating my defeat, and mumbled under my breath, 'Oh balls, you silly old bastard, if you want to call me Pogan I'll let you carry on. Yes sir,' I sighed, dropping my shoulders.

The Judge cracked his face with a false smile.

'Mrs Pogan, you have been summoned to this court hearing by the Newham Council, the charge is, that on the 10th of June you wilfully set out to cause damage to their property by deliberately painting the front door of your house in a bright-green.'

'Garden green, sir.'

'Yes, yes, Mrs Pogan, speak up.'

I made a half-cup with my hand to my mouth in order to throw my echo up to his high chair.

'The colour, sir,' I said, 'it was called garden-green.'

'Who's got a garden?'

'I have, sir – well, a matchbox garden.'

'Mrs Pogan,' interrupted the Judge impatiently, 'Did you or did you not paint your front door green?'

I screwed up my nose with distaste, and replied, 'But I don't like navy-blue.'

'So you think you're better than your neighbours, Mrs Pogan?'

He began stroking a reproduction quill pen, but it was no ordinary pen for the imitation feather was enormous, it went round and round in a full circle, it wobbled in temper at me.

'No, your honour, I am no better than anyone. I am just trying to explain that I don't like dark-blue, it's a depressing colour.'

'Mrs Pogan, did you paint it green in a moment of insanity?'

I got very annoyed at his suggestion.

'No, sir, I most definitely wasn't mad at the time, I knew exactly what I was doing.'

The quill shook violently and his pale face reddened with temper. As the Judge composed himself, he spoke with total indifference.

'I see no point in pursuing this case any further; it's been made clear to this court that Mrs Pogan has no sense of right or wrong; I will now pass sentence.' The Judge gave two short sharp coughs into his rolled thin fingers. 'Mrs Pogan, because of your irresponsible behaviour today it seems you leave me no alternative but to sentence you for life to a top, high flatlet and that you will respectfully hand back to the council the keys belonging to your fine council house.'

I grinned at my inner thought of replying, Oh balls, goatface, you can go stick my house and that stupid plastic feather right up your arse.

*

A real-life great big smile spread across me as I filled the kettle, then, as reality took control of my senses, it was sad and lonely sitting in the kitchen sipping coffee.

There must be a memory somewhere to make me laugh, or can it be true that only fantasy makes my joy? If those be the facts, then I must surely be going barmy.

Three short, light taps on the front-door letter box put a stop to my imagination running amok. As soon as I opened the door a warm, gentle voice crept into the hallway.

'I am Miss Line, the social worker from the London Hospital.'

I grabbed her cold damp hand.

'Oh Margaret, nice to see you, come in.'

Margaret was one of the nice ones, one of the dedicated few. For a brief while we chatted about things of little importance, the weather, the cost of today's bus fares, and so on. Margaret warmed her hands round her hot coffee cup. She was dressed in the uniform of a hippy, floor-length flowered skirt, baggy leather shoulder bag. Margaret walked with long lazy strides, rolling like an old sailor on board ship; her beauty came more from within than from what lay on the surface.

With true feeling she carefully asked me, 'Well, how are you, Rosie?'

'I'm a mess.'

Margaret gave no indication of shock at my reply. She deliberately lowered her voice into a sensitive whisper.

'Why, what have you been up to since my last visit?'

I threw my messy head from side to side.

'Don't know, Margaret, I've been in hospital.'

'Why?'

'I took an overdose.'

'For what reason?'

'I'm just fed up.'

I began to fill the kettle, I had to take her attention away from myself or I knew I would begin to cry.

The following morning came in the morbid colour yellowy-grey. A fine damp mist hung around Kerry Close and the surrounding high-rise buildings. To the right of my silent house stood the Royal Albert Docks which had been half-closed down a year or so earlier, putting thousands of people into the tragic situation of being jobless, with little hope of being employed in the future. The distant docks stood lonely and derelict like a spoiled child's discarded toy. Over the flat rooftops of the dull-designed maisonettes the spider-cranes wept with dusty dew, their long cargo hooks hugging mustard clouds set in a sea of blue and grey specks. Once, only ten minutes' walk away, there was a park full of giant, branchy trees where sparrows sat gossiping all day long, until one beautiful spring day men came carrying razor-sharp electric saws and by the end of the week there was not one tree left standing. A cruel giant had cut a lovely green cake in half and gobbled it into his greedy mouth in order to lay a hard stone highway. When I mentioned to others that I lived at Custom House on the edge of London people seemed amazed that such a town still existed.

Best I not remind myself of such a place ravished by wars and industry. Custom House lies scarred to the core and there seems little hope of its distorted body being covered over by any plastic surgeon.

*

I was living in the spot where Dad was born and raised. My father began his hard working life when he was nine years old. He was absolutely illiterate, for Dad had no opportunity to go to school because the times were of such terrifying poverty. His day began at five o'clock in the morning when Stratford fruit and vegetable market had already been open for an hour. He worked long hard days on an open vegetable stall in Stratford High Street, his grubby thin arms aching, as he stood shaking a wire, circular sieve full of dirty potatoes, jumping up and down, up and down, releasing the hard dry mud from their smooth jackets. The bustling market would rarely close down until the sun had long left the London sky, which meant his day's work would last some twelve hours or so. In winter the frost would bite into his hands like a unfriendly dog. In order to stop the rain penetrating his tiny trembling shoulder blades he would throw an empty potato sack on to his back and by the end of the day it was so full of moisture it felt like a ton weight. Due to the constant child exploitation Father had the posture of an eighty-year-old man when he was no more than forty.

Mother was also born and bred in Custom House but the long, poverty-stricken streets where Mum and Dad served their apprenticeship in life had long since disappeared.

It was now evening time and the windows of my home were covered black on the outside, for I could see nothing, as daylight had left the sky for the night shift of stars which would soon be followed by the silver-faced nightwatchman, alias the moon.

Mark and Sarah, as usual, were watching the bright, square box in the living-room, while I sat vacantly weighing up the events of the day. Margaret Line had phoned to say that she had had a word with Dr Dee at the London Hospital's diabetic clinic (which I had been visiting regularly since I was the tender age of seventeen). Margaret said Dr Dee wanted to see me on the coming Thursday. Jim had phoned me late-afternoon to investigate how I was progressing after my stay at the Romford's suicide ward. I had relayed Margaret's message to him and he, full of concern, had said he would accompany me on the day of my appointment with Dr Dee.

I sat in my still-dark bedroom. The television downstairs was trembling like a non-stop mechanical hound. So intense and vibrating was the constant blast it shook the floorboards beneath my slippered feet. I began to play around with the idea of meeting Dr Dee and my imagination took full command.

Dr Dee was a tall, willowy woman in her late-thirties.

She twisted her lanky legs like a cork-screw, leant forward on her swivel chair and announced, 'Well, Rosie, I'm afraid you have a bad attack of dropsy, it's pretty common these days, all in the mind, you know.'

'Dropsy,' echoed I in surprise, 'I've never heard of it, doctor.'

'Oh yes,' she reassured me. 'As I said, it's very common now, especially in built-up areas such as you live in.' Dr Dee fumbled through my past notes, sticking her sniffing nose only four inches away from the top of her cluttered desk. 'It's simply a way of retreating from society.'

'What are the symptoms, doctor?'

'It all starts when you go out in the morning and your neighbours are walking towards you. To avoid saying hello or good morning they drop their gaze on to the ground because they don't want to communicate with anyone, but the trouble starts, Rosie, when they can't get their eyes back off the ground.'

I smiled with delight, pleased to know I wasn't the only one with such a weird complaint.

'Yes, I know, Dr Dee, for they do it all the time where I live – I thought nobody liked me.'

'No, no, Rosie, each person thinks the same and this is why it's so contagious, we just can't come up with any psychological answer, just can't get their eyes back off the ground. When they try to look up they say the sight of the high flats makes them feel sick.'

'But I live in a house.'

The doctor clasped her hands with joy. 'We can cure you.'

'Cure me? Why's that then?'

'Well, you weren't raised in a high dwelling, this means you are not paranoid about heights.'

The woman was on the verge of hysteria as she yanked hold of my hand.

'Tell me what is it like living on earth-level.'

Her hold got tighter, I felt the hard surface of my wedding ring nip into the flesh of the finger next to it.

'Let go,' yelled I. 'You're some kind of a nutcase, I came here for you to help me, it's like the blind leading the blind in this bloody place.'

CHAPTER FOUR

Thursday came without any hitch and Jim kept his promise. We left Kerry Close just after lunch to make our way to the hospital. I pinched his taut, muscly arm.

'Can you see anyone with dropsy, Jim?'

He looked into my mocking face with bewilderment.

'Do what?' he snapped. 'Dropsy?'

I told Jim not to pursue my question as it was of little consequence whether he understood or not, and to linger on my statement would only make him more confused than he was.

Jim and I travelled swift and silent on the underground train to Whitechapel. Jim, as always, sat quiet and brooding, a man of very few words, not capable of giving me one small crumb of comfort to ease my inner thoughts of despair. I sat on the fast, smoky train wondering if on my arrival at the London Hospital they would pin a label on to me of insanity. I desperately wanted to ask Jim for some kind of help or understanding but our past relationship was so distant and insecure it seemed pretty hopeless us becoming close, as other lovers usually were. The whole pattern of his angry life was well established many years ago before I ever met him. His childhood was surrounded by an overbearing atmosphere of hatred and suspicion created by his selfish parents, whose main goal in life was the disruption of each other. Poor sad Jim, caught in their devious web, was like a feeble insect that had lost its wings, unable to fly away. Now, after living under the same roof for eighteen years long and battling, I still knew nothing of what made Jim tick, for he stood six foot three inches tall, hard as a rock, as though he were encased in a huge granite shell which he most probably built himself when he was a child, sick of being hurt inside. I, a mere uneducated mortal, was not clever or wise enough to chisel away at the stone.

To Jim, every man was a low-life and every woman a whore. Our conflict stemmed from my dreamy attitude to life. I constantly contradicted his philosophy in strongly insisting that each person in the world had a fine noble streak hidden within their make-up and if only given the chance it would come out bright as a newborn star. Or I should say that was once my beautiful belief, because I felt at that moment Jim had won, for I was now totally convinced that this planet was most definitely a great big pisshole and I wanted no part in it.

We arrived at the hospital and I like clockwork joined the sad collection of patients in our monthly ritual of first removing our shoes and stepping on to the iron scales, then entering the toilet and producing a watery tube of warm urine. Then, like speechless zombies, sitting outside the doctor's office for an hour or so. How sick I felt at this boring routine and what a depressing drug insulin must be, for never did I come across so many sad, dull people brought together week after week, year after year.

On the walls of the shiny cream waiting-
room hung oil paintings of every description, portraits, landscapes and abstracts, all
elegantly framed in gold-carved squares. The
paintings that were easily recognised, such
as country scenes and happy faces, gave my
brain relaxation and delight, but oh those
tormenting abstract monstrosities, how they
made me feel inadequate as I sat trying to sort
out their intellectual message, they made me
feel as though I was no more than an idiot
who could not even understand a work of
great art.

After one silent hour I was called in and
led fussily into Dr Dee's office. After seeing
my deathly appearance the doctor began to
take an unfamiliar interest in me, building
her subtle questions up to why I had taken
an overdose of sleeping tablets. I calmly
explained that I thought I was going insane
and couldn't endure the sickness. My bodily
pain was not so bad, for after twenty-two
years of hypo attacks and injections, it was
just a way of life, but my brain was something
different, and my eyes, no, never could I exist
without them.

Dr Dee was extremely curious to know why I thought I was going mad and I explained in the only crazy way I knew how, and this was the first time I had mentioned it to anyone but my inner self. Dr Dee and Jim sat silent on the edge of their steel tubular chairs as I sat whispering my confession. I told them how I had completely lost my sense of concentration as though I were deaf; my favourite television programmes went straight through my head and I could not absorb one word, and the radio played into my brain as though it were empty. I couldn't hear the children, my mother or friends – nothing registered, there was not a trace of communication left in me and the cold realisation of this fact was terrifying my being. I was also constantly forgetting to wash myself and losing things about my house. Once I tormented myself all day trying to recall where I had put a cup of fresh tea. I knew I had prepared it and yet I could not find it. I wondered if I had only imagined it. Then the following day I found it stone-cold in the oven compartment of the cooker.

I could have carried on and on with my list of stupid unexplained actions if Dr Dee had

not politely interrupted with the suggestion
I had a brief chat with a psychiatric man
named Dr Pretty.

Half an hour later Dr Pretty and I were
sitting alone in a vacant examination room
in the diabetic unit, he was cool and full
of self-confidence, an extremely clean-cut
person, very aware of his rather nice profile
and streamlined build. His dress sense was
perfect, he took the utmost care in choosing
his clothing so that each item blended in
with his personality of think well before you
act. When he spoke the lovely velvety tone
filled my emptiness with hope that at last
here was someone who understood. I knew the
gentleness in his voice and manner were false
and probably taught him by some top-dog
professor, but I didn't care, he was so nice,
so caring, that I melted and lost my mask of
strength. I couldn't believe the truth of the
situation: for the first time in my life here
I sat with a strange man I had known for a
brief ten minutes and he really and truthfully
understood enough to do something positive
to help me.

'Rosie,' murmured Dr Pretty as softly as

he could, 'I would like you to come into our psychiatric unit right now.'

I was stunned and speechless for a few moments, turning over in my mind the possibility of being locked up in a madhouse with a load of screaming crazy people. I had to prove my sanity.

'Oh please, I beg of you, please, I am not mad, just empty, that's all.'

My words fell from my lips without control. Dr Pretty sat, full of interest, allowing me to ramble on and on as if a thick, heavy, locked gate had been opened letting the water flow non-stop into the waiting peacefulness of a silent stream.

'I am not the only one, Dr Pretty,' I assured him, tossing my head back in defiance. 'There are hundreds in this world like me, we don't like living and I don't see why people should force us to keep in the game if we don't like what they are playing at. I think there should be some kind of institution set up for us, where we can go and state our reason for not living and then they should give us six months for our next appointment, then if we still feel the same about living you should help us, and prescribe something quick and efficient. Who are these do-gooders who say we should live and suffer, whether we like it or not?'

The more Dr Pretty pursued the question of my being admitted into hospital, the more I felt lost and helpless. I desperately needed someone to lean on for moral support, so I suggested that I talk the matter over with Jim, who had sat patient through the complicated process.

Jim made my mind up for me, assuring me that he would return home to care for Mark and Sarah while I was away. Everything was arranged for the following morning, the name of the psychiatric ward was Rachel, and I was to be there before lunch.

I begged Jim, whatever happened to me while I was away, he must promise never to sign any papers on my behalf, because no matter how strange my behaviour seemed on the surface, I was not and never would be insane. I'd heard horrifying stories of people being signed away to a life of hell. Once when I was very young I saw a very disturbing film, *The Snakepit*. It was all about a woman who was perfectly sane, suffering only a bad case of nervous tension. They placed her in a ward full of wild crazy women and by the end of the story she was tormented into madness.

Jim, in full view of the bustling hospital, held me so tight, enough to crush my trembling shoulders.

'Rosie, trust me,' he whispered. 'I may be a bastard at times but underneath it all, I love you more than I love myself.' Jim pushed his straight bony nose on to mine, his watery eyes just a fraction of an inch away from mine. 'And you know more than anyone how much I book myself.'

I smiled at his remark, for he had such an air of comedy in the few words he spoke. His large dark eyes reminded me of a spaniel dog, all limp and loyal. I was on the verge of submitting to his loving gaze.

No, Rosie, now watch yourself, how many times have you been screwed up inside because you were foolish enough to put complete trust in certain people, and Jim is the worst culprit of all, absolutely unpredictable, a man who has the power to build you sky high, only to pull you down with a sickening thud.

Jim stayed with me all night, trying in his immature way to comfort me, but he was just not wise enough to answer one burning question.

If eyes are the mirror of the soul, then if the eyes become dead, does the soul die also?

When I thought of the way I had wasted my eyesight it filled me with disgust and remorse, I never bothered to notice the colour of a sparrow's eye, or the day-by-day growth of a bright flower. My eyes were far too busy gazing into shop windows with my stupid heart longing to own a dazzling expensive gown or a pair of high-fashion shoes, my eyes were no more than something to be painted and fussed over. I would smother my eyelids with bright-green or sky-blue, whatever colour was the fashion. Like an over-age puppet I tried to keep in step with the younger generation. All the writing I could have done and the wonderful things I could have used as subjects for my books.

CHAPTER FIVE

Friday morning leapt upon me with such
bustling speed that it left me breathless and
panic-stricken. I had bathed and washed my
neglected mop of black greasy hair, had my
daily injection, packed my necessary belongings into a small white suitcase, fed Penny
and Blossom with a can of anaemic meat
chunks, and then flopped down into a kitchen
chair puffing on my tipped cigarette like a
condemned woman, ready to be taken into
Rachel.

Jim and I arrived at the hospital in good
time. Jim dragged me hesitantly along the
rubber-cushioned corridor leading to Rachel.
On entering, a young buxom nurse greeted
us by introducing herself as Sue. Jim was
as confused as I on meeting Sue for she was

not dressed in the regular attire of starch and disinfectant, she had on a modern, calf-length skirt topped by a clinging red sweater. Her thick, healthy brown hair was cut short and frizzed into African style and even more to our amazement Sue had a long-tipped cigarette stuck between her podgy little fingers. She told us to sit on the warm, flowered easy chairs outside Dr Bright's office, which lay directly inside the ward's entrance.

The time was around noon and from somewhere within the silent ward a voice screamed, 'Tablets – tablets!' A few moments later the door in front of us opened like a stable. The bottom half was shut but the top swung open to reveal Sue the nurse standing like a sweet-kiosk assistant surrounded by bottles of bright-coloured pills. A weird collection of men and women crawled like uninterested snails and hung around Sue with their white palms open waiting to catch their medication. They didn't look at the two strangers intruding into their camp, it made me feel invisible as their dead glassy eyes passed straight through my being. Everything seemed unreal and strange, especially when

Dr Bright came on to the scene looking like she had just stepped off the glossy cover of a fashion magazine.

'Rose, would you come into my office?' asked Dr Bright with a voice as sweet as honey.

She gave Jim an ashtray, inviting him to smoke if he so wished. She was a female Dr Pretty, drawing words from my lips, building me with an unfamilar confidence. At one point she even made me burst into a flood of long-awaited tears, which gave me great relief.

I couldn't help but admire how clever they were with words, yes, two of the young doctors I had encountered so far were most certainly pretty bright.

Dr Bright had a thick folder on the desk in front of her. It contained all my history compiled at the diabetic unit.

She stopped half-way through the mass of paper and asked, 'I see by your notes, Rosie, that you have always preferred to have high blood sugar.'

'Preferred?' snapped I. 'That's a joke.'

Dr Bright leaned foward and looked straight into my face.

'Would you like to tell me about it, Rosie?'

I began to explain the events leading up to my ill health and how I, through the fault of circumstances, was unable to control my diabetes.

It was because I did not want Mark and Sarah to experience what I did as a child, coming home from school never to find any warmth, nothing but a cold, empty house with a sink full of dirty breakfast plates to be washed, and a quarter-hundredweight of coal to be carried from a far-off shop on my freezing back, through rain or snow, hands numb with the cold and my plimsoled feet soaked to the bone. My favourite brother Dennis would remove my soaking slippers and rub my feet with his fast, strong hands, making my skinny toes tingle with warm circulation. I made an oath to Dennis at the time, saying I would never, if I had children of my own, make them endure such total emptiness, for I would always be waiting for them, when they came home from school in the bitter winter, with a steaming-hot cup of tea and buttered crumpets.

But to find a job from ten to three each day was hard. The only way I could keep my promise was to be a barmaid at lunchtimes, and what a strange selfish breed of people publicans were. I had not yet come across one of them who did not suffer from money mania, so greedy was their nature. They without conscience would encourage a hard-working man to spend his wage packet on drink, leaving his waiting family at home penniless. Publicans thought nothing of using a young girl in order to attract men to spend their hard-earned income in the public house: topless go-go dancers, strippers, people used like a commodity to entice poverty into others' homes. And even bar staff were paid slave-wages, working five hours a day for the sum of £1.25, rarely was one offered food or a short rest, for publicans were parasites.

So how on earth could I expect compassion from my boss when I felt ill as I was serving behind the bar? Could anyone imagine me saying, I am going hypo, please can I rest for ten minutes? The greedy opportunist would burst into tears, as he reckoned up how many whiskies I could put over the counter in ten

minutes, and to ask for something to eat would
make the poor man grieve for the loss of a ham
roll. So over the years if I should become hypo
and on the verge of unconsciousness, there
was always in my bag a sugary Mars bar
or glucose, which was deadly to my health.
What a pity men born in the East End could
only achieve success by being a common
publican, for this was the only business that
needed neither education nor brains, and
what a shame so many got caught up in the
inescapable maze of greed. I despised being
part of such a set-up, but when you wanted a
crust, you didn't allow conscience to interfere
with the grinding wheel of fortune, or should
I say your survival.

There existed one exception to my distaste
for publicans, a pair of people named Jenny
and Jack, who after three years in the pub
game still stood uncorrupted by greed, and I
prayed for Jenny as often as I could remember,
hoping she and Jack would not end up like
overdressed Christmas trees like so many
of their successful comrades, who took great
pains in displaying their instant wealth as
though it were some great gift from heaven.

I got a lot of pleasure myself from drink, but I would sooner be a consumer, rather than have the burden of the unlikeable supplier. For so much grief and hardship in the world existed over drink. I was quite sure I would crack beneath my conscience.

Dr Bright listened attentively and gave no comment. She looked extremely pleased with me, happy that she had successfully scratched the surface of the chain of events leading up to my mental disorder. I was sure my problems were real, something Dr Bright could get her hungry teeth into, not abstract like those of so many of the other patients crawling round the ward, with their hanging heads crammed full of fantasy and illusions.

I am real.

Jim and I were taken by Nurse Sue to be shown round Rachel. Just past the dispensary and Dr Bright's office lay the kitchen where Italian-speaking orderlies were chatting above the clatter of crockery. Next to the kitchen was Sister's office. The rest of the long ward was separated by a thick wall and in the centre was a wide, doorless gap which allowed the men admittance into the women's unit and vice versa.

The patients' sleeping quarters were made up into double units, each one well-surrounded for privacy. The decor of the homely little bedrooms was of a rich red polished wood. There were gay-patterned bedspreads on short-legged divans with smart modern headboards, a compact living-space which would give delight to any child, with miniature dressing-tables and wardrobes. To give added privacy there was a beautiful, grained five-foot wall running the length of the soft-carpeted corridor. So intimate were the surroundings I felt privileged to join the clan.

When Jim and I reached the end of the bedroom, the place opened up to reveal a huge lounge full of all kinds of easy chairs – there were high ones, low ones, flowered pieces and tapestry. A very elegant colour television stood in one corner beside an equally smart radiogram. Every item was warm and welcoming, reds, browns and yellows, even the large, bright-green table-tennis board fitted into the picture with ease. Above the empty play-table hung a long collection of two-foot-square water-colour paintings so bizarre in colour and design that Jim gave a short blast of laughter at the mad arrows and flowers. Jim remarked that they all looked like they came from some other planet. Next to the lounge was the dining-room, also of a homely nature, where funny tame mice played hide-and-seek through the nights with Sister Kate and Male Nurse Peter, who I had not yet had the happy experience of meeting.

I didn't know till later in the day that at the beginning of each corridor stood two private rooms for patients who needed extra special handling – little did I expect to be classified as one of these.

My room was as nice as all the other open compartments. I had my own personal hot and cold taps and wash basin, and my bed was an old-type, tall hospital bed painted sickly cream, the paint scratched in places, presumably where it had been wheeled round and round the hospital, probably over a great number of years. I couldn't believe I was in hospital, for the surroundings confused my memories of long periods of being hospitalised

where everything was white, and nurses quick-
stepped, faceless, in and out of your vision,
like crisply starched uniforms, and you never
knew their names or their true identity. Here
today the nurses were real: people of colour.
I kept telling myself this was a dream and I
should wake up very soon.

By late afternoon Jim had left, promising
he would return later with the children.

A petite, dark-skinned Indian nurse led me
into the lounge which she explained was
called the day room. Her thin frame was so
delicate and her small hands so sensitively
gentle like a bird's wing, I immediately nick-
named her Sparrow. She placed me in a beautifully soft, beige-coloured chair and then set
about introducing me to the still patient at
my side, whose name was Lydia. Lydia was
English but very dark, a highly strung woman
in her late-thirties. When Sparrow left our
company Lydia asked why I had been brought
into Rachel. I told her in a shameful whisper
of how I had tried to commit suicide.

'Oh, I've tried that,' shrugged Lydia with
contempt.

She showed me her mutilated wrist distorted with deep ugly scars. Lydia sat so composed, and her attitude to death was so calm and relaxed, I had to know more. I asked her why she was in Rachel. Her reply made me shudder with fear.

'Oh me, I am very violent.' Her voice was flat without any change of tone. She continued, 'I tried to murder my child.'

When I asked how, Lydia told me many times she had nearly beaten the tiny infant to death, but the last time she tried to strangle him, and would have succeeded had not her family pulled her off.

Never had I heard of such unashamed violence, panic writhing and pounding inside my breast. I spoke no more and Lydia glided off into her sleeping space.

I sat shocked and dazed, asking myself what I was doing in such a place.

Am I part of this whole bizarre set-up or am I no more than an innocent onlooker? Yes, that's it, I am watching one of those silly 'Carry on' films, the title must surely be *Carry on Crazy*.

'Why are you trying to kill me?' asked a

woman standing directly in front of me. Her eyes were icy-cold pools of anguish. She was sneering at me not with hatred but with absolute terror.

'Why are you trying to kill my children?'

Her question was interrupted by Sparrow who sat down beside me throwing her feeble voice across my throbbing chest.

'Now, sit down, Frenchie, and behave yourself,' commanded Sparrow to the disturbed woman. 'Rosie is a new patient and she is also not very well, so I don't think you should annoy her with your French Algerians.'

The more I sat observing all that was going on around my person, the more I wanted to stay, to investigate the place of freedom, where people travelled undisturbed into another world, far more terrifying than I could ever imagine.

By what strange route do these poor beings travel, is it through a long dark tunnel of uncontrollable events, or are they born like this?

I had to find out the answer, for my whole being needed so desperately to know.

I can take plenty of stick, so don't you worry about me, little Sparrow, for I can take as much crazy verbal as anyone in this hostile place can dish out. In any case I'm dead already so who on this mad, mad earth has enough strength to hurt me?

My sudden burst of fear and panic subsided. I tucked my long thin legs under my bottom, dropped my puzzled head to one side and closed my heavy eyelids, for I wanted to think and investigate all my mixed-up feelings. I couldn't understand why I felt this warm flow of compassion and pity, it was outweighing the fear I had experienced on meeting Lydia and Frenchie.

Is it normal to feel so peaceful over such an experience, or is it all just because I can't see their hollow-eyed, distorted faces? Could be I am lucky after all.

Every time I used my brain my body automatically became drained of energy. I wanted to sleep so I begged Sparrow to guide me to my room as I was not yet familiar with my new surroundings. I sank on to the bed, exhausted, for I had been introduced to far too many new people for my numbed brain to cope with, and now I felt I must go blank, by passing into the safe cavern of sleep where true thoughts could rest in comfort, and fantasy play hide-and-seek with the unconscious.

CHAPTER SIX

'Wake up! Wake up!' I was being shouted
and tugged at by someone I had never heard
before.

'I am Lucy,' whispered she, placing her
finger over her lips. 'We have landed in
California, come on, quick, get up before the
ship leaves without us.'

My heart leapt out to the beautiful young
woman before me. Lucy was twenty years
old with huge round amber eyes and painted
beneath them on her high-boned cheeks was
a shower of heavy blue tears. Her exquisitely
shaped lips were dry and peeling, her bottom lip hung low and drooping. Lucy stood
swaying on her bare feet trying to make sense
with a song, but it was very difficult because
her childish voice was slurred with drugs, or

so it seemed. She thrust open her arms and protruded her well-rounded breasts, like a fine opera singer about to give the greatest performance of her life. Lucy's voice was not so hot, but the energy and feeling she put into the song simply tore at the heartstrings.

'I am so tired of living and so scared of dying, but old man river, he just keeps rolling along.' Lucy ended her performance with a soft ripple of crazy laughter.

I was well awake by now, in fact it was the most awake I had been for a long long time. I held out my hand to the bloodstained ghost of a person and introduced myself.

'Hello, Lucy, I am Rosie, your song was beautiful.' I punched at my heart and grinned. 'It got me right there, Lucy.'

Lucy squeezed my hand and asked me, 'Who are you? Are you part of *This Is Your Life*?' She recognised my puzzlement by my cocking my head to one side and squinting. 'I bet it is you,' Lucy continued with excitement. 'That television show, you know, Eamonn Andrews, he's coming here to do *This Is Your Life*, and it's all about you, ain't it?'

I took no heed of her daydream, for although

Lucy was offering me an open invitation to her wonderful world of songs, sailing ships and film stars, I didn't feel quite ready to join her. I could only give my attention to Lucy's real person.

'How long have you been in Rachel?' I asked.

Lucy didn't seem to have the ability to answer my question, as though out of step with time. She leapt ahead, giving replies only to what she felt in your eyes. She pointed to her cheeks.

'Look,' she said, 'today I am sad, my tears are blue.'

Then Lucy without any explanation took to her wobbly heels and fled from my room. I immediately understood her frustrated behaviour, for she, the same as myself, found it extremely hard to concentrate for lengthy periods of time.

The weekend passed with different nurses, male and female, taking, in constant rotation, the morbid pleasure of my company, so obvious was their endeavour to build up some sort of friendship. It made me smile at the thought that they should think me such a fool as not to notice they were merely compiling my behaviour and way of thinking for the purpose of relating the information to the doctor's report on the following Monday. The pattern was always the same. I would be sitting quietly alone, but not for long, because someone would casually flop down in the empty chair beside me.

'Oh dear,' he or she would sigh, 'my feet are killing me,' or some other reference to exhaustion on their part. Then the conversation would inconspicuously begin to revolve around how I felt and why did I wind up in Rachel.

I gave each interrogator the same story, and towards the end of the day I felt like a well-rehearsed actress, repeating the same old lines over and over again.

I was glad when Monday came bright and buzzing with a host of new voices. They belonged to other patients who had gone home for a short weekend, and a few day-patients who came each morning to sit through one hour of group therapy, also psychiatric doctors, and a bright band of day-sisters and staff.

One voice above all others could be heard all over the ward, even if you were sitting on the toilet having a quiet little puff on a cigarette. The over-loud tones belonged to Long Dog. She was the therapist, a woman in her early-forties, a little over six-foot tall, lanky as a lamppost. Her face was nice in a well-scrubbed sort of way, but her large blue eyes sank very often with loneliness, but only when Long Dog was caught off guard, for she took great pride in the impression she gave to others who thought her capable of handling any situation that might arise.

Each day Long Dog would organise drama or exercises for us reluctant patients. At ten o'clock each morning many of us, including myself, would scamper away like naughty children trying to avoid Long Dog's hour of therapy. Lucy and I always hid in the waiting room just outside the ward; Empty, a quiet man, chose the toilet. Frenchie would escape into a bathful of hot water, poor thing, for after one whole hour the water would be cold. God, a man of twenty-six, never bothered to hide, for when Long Dog went sniffing round Rachel ferreting out her missing subjects, she knew from past experience not to bother God. Many times before she had interfered with God's solitude and always his angry feedback has been, 'Bollocks – bollocks.' Some of us may have tried dodging the ten to eleven body exercises, but no one with the exception of Lucy ever backed away from the daily eleven to twelve group therapy.

I was about to encounter for the first time the peculiar personalities revealed inside the private circle, where no man could intrude, unless by the cruel hand of fate he was dragged in by the scruff of his mental disorder. The circle of human suffering was made up of two or three doctors, sometimes a student of psychology, Long Dog, and from a dozen to twenty patients.

Everyone sat speechless and motionless, the only sound within reach of my ear was the constant stream of heavy traffic roaring back and forth along the busy Whitechapel Road outside. Every person's face was dead and lifeless as if waiting for some huge hand up above to pull the strings.

I wonder if they all feel the same as I, like a soft pink snail who is so easy to squash, boneless, spiritless, retreating back into the security of my shell if anyone should attack, but the hard shell I carry is heavy on my aching back and it weighs me down, for my soft spineless body is too weak for such a heavy burden. Who put salt on my tail, making me shrivel up into my shell? There is no one I can point my accusing finger at except society in general.

I wanted to break the silence by saying something that would most definitely label me as mad, or a sex maniac or even a lesbian.

Oh balls, I'll break this silence.

I lifted my head high, opened my eyes as wide as possible and announced, 'I want to be held. Is there anyone in this group who will let me sit on their lap and will they please caress me without sex coming into the scene.'

Someone shifted nervously, others had a bad attack of dropsy.

'I will, Rosie,' yelled God, 'for I love everyone.'

I rose to my feet and walked slowly across

the shocked circle to God. He weighed somewhere in the region of nine stone, my bony
bottom slid on to his equally bony knees.
God's face was unusually small, with the
most sensitive eyes I had ever come across.
God held me, protective, like my father used
to when I was a child.

God then gently cupped my face with his
trembling hands, kissed my fringed forehead
and softly whispered, 'Rosie, I love you.'

'Oh.' I began sobbing. 'Oh, it's so nice to
be held.'

Lucy stomped into the day room to witness
me being cuddled by God. My head was
fitted snug on to his shoulder and while
I sobbed he tenderly stroked my rocking
back.

'Hey, Stumbles,' yelled Lucy, rushing over
to get a better view. She had christened
me Stumbles over the weekend, after I had
accidentally walked into a piano, a serving
trolley, and a Chinese porter. 'What you
doing with God?'

'I'm being loved,' choked I.

Lucy giggled. 'I am going to have some
of that,' and she pounced on Dr Scramble,

glaring at him like he was a plate of tempting food.

Dr Scramble's reaction was not what it should have been, for he was a qualified psychiatrist able to cope with any run-of-the-mill group behaviour. Dr Scramble was slight in build, hiding under a brown wiry beard and thick, black-rimmed spectacles, a quiet man who with elastic steps glided in and out of Rachel with his frail head hung forward, knowing more about a person's footwear than anyone else in the hospital.

By now hungry Lucy was sitting on Dr Scramble's shaking knees, with his thick black spectacles balanced on the end of her small snub nose. The first three buttons of his striped shirt were undone, revealing a pure-white pigeon chest. Lucy sat running her fingers through his fuzzy chin-growth.

Lucy's voice was low and seductive:

'Come on, Scrambles, let yourself go.'

She began to undo yet another button, and this was the last straw. He panicked, jumped to his feet, and fled, letting Lucy crash on to the floor with a painful thud.

'You bastard,' screamed Lucy, unsorting

her position, and then standing angrily with her hands resting on her plump hips. 'I'm going to get you.'

Whether she kept her threat no one knew. Screaming, Lucy pursued Scrambles' speedy heels along the corridor of Rachel.

A lonely middle-aged woman called across the circle, 'I always wanted a baby to love, but I can't conceive one, my husband won't forgive me for not giving him a child.'

Young Sue, a slim mousy girl of sixteen, ran towards the barren woman and flung her spider-thin arms around the woman's neck.

'My mother never loved me,' wept Sue.

Each patient emptied their inner self and the response spread like a haystack fire, all were happy and glowing with warmth. All except Long Dog, until a tall, good-looking cockney with a voice rough as sandpaper grabbed her tense hands, jerking Long Dog on to her feet and making her snooty head jump forward. So crude was the lustful man's approach, I was surprised by the instant beam of delight that spread across Long Dog's face like a ray of long-awaited sunshine, especially after he, in such an insensitive manner, suggested that they have it away somewhere because he had fancied giving Long Dog one for a long time.

How I love my world of fantasy where I'm completely free, for when true life gets too brutal I can always ease the pain by escaping through the dark barrier of time into a world of my own choosing.

Long Dog's loud, scolding voice interrupted my trip to dreamland. She was glaring at Lucy, who was kneeling on the floor taking the whole group's attention. Lucy was singing, 'I beg your pardon, I never promised you a rose garden,' as she sat shaking a three-pence blue-and-white-striped plastic carrier bag, tipping its entire contents on to the floor. Lucy had brought instant chaos, for the bag contained some small precious item from each patient's private bed unit: toothpaste, writing books, hairbrush, aftershave, and far too many other pieces to mention, and yet not one angry person came forward to repossess their borrowed belongings. It was all left to the uneasy staff, I couldn't believe it, they were all terrified of crazy giggling Lucy.

Long Dog growled, 'Lucy, will you please leave the group if you're going to act crazy.'

I wanted to shout on Lucy's behalf, telling them to leave her be, for at least she had brought us zombies back to life for a short while after we had been sitting speechless for some twenty minutes. But I was a mere spectator, and knew nothing of Lucy's illness, so I sat quiet leaving the problem to the qualified doctors and nurses. After a screaming scuffle with a half-frightened nurse, Lucy was allowed to keep the borrowed contents of her over-loaded bag, and the other patients to whom they belonged were reassured their property would be returned after Lucy was restrained and gently persuaded to see the confusion created in the ward because of her wild behaviour.

A few moments after Lucy's rowdy departure, God stood dressed in a well-laundered candlewick dressing-gown which hung loose and baggy over his small frail body. As he opened his arms and legs wide apart, a short blast of stomach wind rolled beneath his shabby attire. Long Dog and I were the only two who found it hard not to laugh.

'I am God, do you hear me? I died for you.'

No one took the slightest bit of notice. Every piece of flesh on God's body was trembling as he marched round the circle pointing a long white finger at each of us in turn saying with dead-faced fury, 'I died for you.' Then suddenly, as if someone had waved a powerful magic wand, God seemed to get bored with his bizarre behaviour. He turned and left the disinterested group and briskly headed towards the kitchen, his angry words echoing all through the ward.

'Bollocks – bollocks – bollocks.'

I sat stunned and strangely stimulated. It was like living inside a real dream.

Where am I and what's it all about?

I wondered if these weird characters were planted inside Rachel in order to prove just how much aggravation someone could stand before they eventually cracked.

Each evening an army of visitors would arrive like a swarm of sight-seeing infants let loose inside a live theatre of temperamental actors and actresses exhibiting their inner talent.

On Wednesday nights there would be a social gathering organised by Long Dog: there was indoor hockey, piano-playing, sandwiches and tea, everything to make patients and visitors harmonise. Even this sensible idea of communication was madly reversed, for the patients would sit and make common-sense remarks while the visitors from the calm sane world outside pranced around the day room yelling and screaming as they enthusiastically tried to beat a pair of old socks squashed up into a scraggy ball with a rolled-up newspaper for a hockey stick. Most of the time us patients never saw our visitors for they were always paying the valuable attention to each other. But I liked the set-up, especially when all the patients would gather in my room, making lovely comments about the visitors who never bothered to find out where we were spending our time on the social evenings.

Jim and the children came to see me each evening from seven till nine. Like three thirsty desert camels, they drank countless pots of tea and coffee. I think it was the bright silver tea urn standing in the kitchen, singing with instant hot water, that fascinated Jim. I was always happy to see my family and yet even happier when they left for home – I could still see no future for my passionless body outside of Rachel.

I was becoming more and more confident each day, for I had taught myself the way to the toilet and kitchen. I also knew where the drugs room was. This was the easiest for all I had to do was to follow the familiar scream. Four times daily the nurse would yell out, 'Tablets, tablets,' like a keeper at the zoo who calls the seals, throwing silver fish down to their sad-eyed faces.

I also trained my bladder to produce a specimen of sugary urine every four hours. Like a clockwork toy, I lay on my bed waiting for a nurse to come and wind me up for breakfast, dinner, tea time, blood tests, and so on. My sleep each night lasted for no more than four or five hours, and I couldn't bring myself to sleep without the light on for I was unexplainably afraid of darkness and all its weird noises: young teenagers sobbing, men screaming and dragging insomnia footsteps. At least my fear was silent and not upsetting to others.

My despair came from inside. I was going blind without any form of pain to my body, except for a daily surface injection. The only real pain was what I created inside my own self, and yet I could control my hurt enough not to cause pity from others. How unbearable then was the hurt of those around me now, that they could not help crying in the night, grown men sobbing like frightened children. How strong must their hurt have been, how did you become broken and spiritless, void of all feeling and passion, just existing instead of living, for I knew they were not born that way.

How do you become drained of love? Are there human blood suckers who sap every drop of emotion from another's being until the victim is left empty inside?

Every morning as the sleepy London sparrows were shaking their grubby feathers and stretching their frosty wings in readiness for a new scrounging day, Lucy woke after sleeping her medication away. And each dark morning she cried out for help.

'Dad – Dad, where's my dad? Oh please, Dad, help me.'

Lucy occupied the private room opposite mine, and I never closed my door, for this was another thing that frightened me. I wish I had a pair of ear plugs, is what I told myself each time Lucy's cries awoke me.

CHAPTER SEVEN

'Stumbles – Stumbles! Wake up,' hissed Lucy
as she burst into my room. But I was fully
awake for it was just after eleven o'clock at
night, far too early for me to close my blank
harsh eyes. I was standing near-naked at the
sink, wearing a pair of the briefest of briefs,
and a scanty blue lace bra.

Lucy's interruption of my nightly washing
process seemed to stir a sense of hostility
within me because I couldn't tell what she
was looking at. I automatically turned to
my sense of smell, which was growing more
powerful with every passing day. I had begun
to pay much attention to my body, covering
myself with soft perfumed talcum powders
and anti-deodorants, for I still had enough
self-respect not to let myself smell of stale

sweat and tobacco, after all I was puffing away on sixty cigarettes daily.

Lucy marched towards my stooping frame in her usual brazen manner. 'Stumbles, I think there's a mouse in my bed.' Suddenly she stopped short and gasped in over-emphasised horror. I felt her trembling curious fingers run across my left shoulder with the superb sensitivity of a butterfly's wing.

'What's this on your back, Stumbles?'

Lucy was referring to a scar, a fine, six-inch scar sunk into a deep crater.

'Oh that,' shrugged I calmly. 'It was a growth I had cut out in this hospital last year.' I continued to rub the back of my wet neck with a coarse-washed ward towel.

Lucy then jerked the right flap of my ear with the innocent brutality of an over-inquisitive child.

Once again she openly asked, 'What's that behind your ear? Is that the reason you wear your hair long, so that it won't show?'

Being as when I was first admitted into Rachel I was silent as a grave and being as it was the constant childish help of Lucy that had encouraged me to come out of my snail's shell and talk a little more freely, I thought my interrogator quite within her rights in asking for the truth. I sighed deep at the memory of the small thick raised line behind my ear. Someone had smashed a glass ashtray into it. I spun round, puffing my hairy armpits with lemon spray powder.

Lucy's voice jerked and stammered with compassion.

'Oh Stumbles, your belly.'

Before Lucy could force another sound from within her shocked brain, I interrupted in carefree spirit but stern.

'That's where I had two Caesareans, it was the only way I could have children. I wouldn't have Mark and Sarah if it wasn't for them scars.'

I pulled my nightdress over my head and slipped it over my perfumed body, while Lucy stood watching my every motion. Her head dropped to one side and her amber-bright eyes puzzled at my cool reaction to all her solemn questions.

She spoke quiet and sad.

'But Stumbles, you are all stitched together.'

'Like a rag doll,' said I, smiling.

Lucy for a few minutes had switched on to being an adult, but from her panicking attitude I could tell she did not like the real situation, not one little bit. So once-grave, sensible Lucy jumped happily back to childhood with just one short blink of her beautiful, damp, milk-chocolate eyes. She giggled mischievously and stuck a cold soft daffodil behind my cheek.

'There, now you look beautiful.'

The heavy yellow trumpet flopped forward, slid along my startled face and on to the floor.

'Oh shit,' growled Lucy, placing the yellow blossom back into the top crease of my ear. 'Tell you what, if it drops out of your ear again we can forget it, because you haven't got to wear flowers where we are going.'

'But Lucy, where are we going?' asked I, full of doubt.

'Shush,' whispered Lucy, pressing her full lips with her forefinger, 'it's my secret place and I'm going to take you there to make you better, but first we must go and wake God up because I know he will want to come.'

'Oh no, Lucy,' begged I. 'Don't let's get into any more trouble, honest, the nurses are doing their nuts over us two. Let God sleep, don't wake him.'

But Lucy would not listen to my caution, she insisted that all the staff including Dr Scramble had told her she could visit the secret place of comfort whenever she so wished.

Why I followed so willingly down the river of madness will always remain a mystery to me. God was not asleep, he was far from it, as he lay on his bed with his pale-blue eyes burning into the pages of an obscene paperback book full of naked women with great bursting breasts and buttocks. As he glared at the juicy magazine his hand was tucked inside the front opening of his red-striped pyjamas, gently stroking his spiritless genitals. When Lucy enquired if he would like to join us, God did not reply. To be truthful, we did not really expect him to talk, for he didn't often answer.

The three of us crept past Night Sister's office like a quiet crafty trio of naughty truanters. When outside the sleepy walls of Rachel, we sighed with cunning relief and lit up a cigarette. Half-way down the long straight corridor Lucy stopped and hissed.

'In here, quick.'

She pushed dumb God and me into an unfamiliar doorway. Lucy then gave orders for us to join our hands together into a human chain, our rigid nerves passing through it like the cold clammy current of an electric eel. It was decided that I should be placed in the middle, being as I was nearly blind, and God at the far end because he was trembling with fright. The damp, musky passageway was long, twisting and dark. On tall, iron-framed shelves behind and to the front of us was a weird, grubby collection of disused hospital equipment. Great cobweb bed specimen jars, rusty remnants of plumbing pipes, boxes of nuts and bolts and old books. It smelt of dust and decay, but there was yet another smell creeping into my blowing nostrils. It was the over-polished scent of the front parlour, where my dead father had lain, when I was a child. My heart pumped inside my sweating breasts, like the thud,

thud of the enormous pile-driving equipment, driving into the red clay like the huge finger of progress, poking the soil in readiness for another tower dwelling of high-rise flats.

'Let's go back,' whispered I, trying to break the black silence of fear we were all three engulfed in.

'Don't be daft, Stumbles,' laughed Lucy, squeezing my hand, hard enough to break the bones. 'We are here now.'

Lucy stood at a wide heavy door and slowly turned the stiff brass handle. She stepped inside boldly.

'Come on, you two,' Lucy beckoned, and dragged us in like two helpless puppets.

The aroma of dried lavender was so strong it tickled the tiny hairs inside my nose, enough to make me cut the thickness of the scented air with a short sharp sneeze.

'Bless you,' grinned Lucy.

We were standing beside a long, plat-formed altar so simple yet so indescribably beautiful. Lucy had led us into the hospital chapel, by a familiar route otherwise only used by the priests, for the public entrance was at the very top of the neat circular seats, sensibly designed so that all the people could see the charming altar below. The simple holy chamber was set more like a high personal theatre than a chapel, but in any event the tiny place of worship was too beautiful for words.

In fact, the sudden view of such warm beauty forced upon the sick mind of our trembling companion proved too much for him to take, he sank on to his bony knees like a burst balloon. Limp, shrivelled, and flat, able to move not one muscle of his sagging form, God was dragged by Lucy and me to the nearest chair, and propped up in full view of the altar. I sat beside him and now he was not soft any more but settled rigid. I felt cold beside God's stone-blank gaze, a young man dreading the thought of what cruel mischief Lucy and I had brought upon his ill health tonight.

Lucy pranced up the two long, red-carpeted steps to the altar.

She sang light and sweet, 'I beg your pardon, I never promised you a rose garden.'

As she sang she danced with clumsy sincerity.

I stretched out my hand and clutched God's taut clenched fists. He did not stir, he just sat there staring into the unknown dungeons of space. I smiled deep into where I thought his eyes to be and held his stiff hand, gently saying, 'Don't worry, you are going to get better soon.'

Something faint and warm hit the back of my hand then flowed in gentle spasms through the creases of my fingers. The stone figure of a man at my side sniffed and choked as if something were trapped inside him, clawing and fighting to try and push past. Great lumps of despair held fast in his anguished throat. My silent friend was weeping, not crying or sobbing, but pure soft weeping, and what had flowed on to my hand and caressed my fingers so beautifully were the tears of the man's sorrow.

Lucy called out from the soft red steps of the altar on which she was now lying seductively stretched, 'We best be getting back to Rachel now before they send out a search party to round up us crazy people.'

As God and I stood to our feet, Lucy walked towards us offering aid, she then smiled and gave a knowing wink into the direction of God's tear-drenched face.

'You are in our gang now, ain't he?'

'Of course,' whispered I, returning Lucy's warm smile.

She leaned forward, spread her fleshy arms over our bent shoulders like men do on a rugby field in order to whisper their next defence or attack, whatever the case may be. Lucy spoke low and soft looking alternately into God's and my eyes.

'Don't tell anyone where we went tonight or they may think we are mad.'

CHAPTER EIGHT

After spending a few weeks inside the intimacy
of Rachel's truthful atmosphere I found my
senses, together with my once-dormant mind,
were as sharp and alert as a fox at the height
of the hunting season. I was engulfed in
love for my fellow sufferers. Frenchie, Lucy,
God, Bones, Empty and Lonely all filled me
with such a bond of honest friendship that
I was forgetting myself. No more were my
thoughts of pity and hurt wrapped around
my sad being, for I was far too engrossed
in their inner loneliness to have time to sit
and ponder away at my own tragedy.

Frenchie was forever coming into my room
carrying a tray neatly arranged with a pot of
hot tea plus an earthenware jug of milk, cups
and saucers.

'Would you like some tea, Rosie?' she would sweetly enquire.

Frenchie's beautiful soothing tone was to be well expected for she once had taken a full course in becoming a qualified barrister. Because she was brilliant, I am sure she would have been very successful, had she not impulsively thrown all her knowledge away by marrying a hot-blooded young man with only one hundreth of her own intelligence.

Frenchie was short and plump and dressed like a frumpish school mistress. I was horrified to discover she was only forty years old, for her short, heavily lacquered hair was pure grey. I was even more disturbed when she told me her hair had changed from rich chestnut-brown to dull iron-grey only three months earlier, at the beginning of her nervous breakdown.

I learned that Frenchie had once been a dedicated, loving mother of six children, living happily in an expensive, well-furnished house on the outskirts of London. After years of constant brutality inflicted upon her person by her unkind husband, Frenchie

understandably cracked under the indescribable torment. Frenchie now wandered round
and round the passageways of Rachel like
a chain-smoking half-wit, and had done
so for the past three months. The terror
reflected in her small brown eyes was of
her own making, for she was constantly
being chased and threatened by a vicious
gang of cunning, cruel French Algerians
who wanted to kill and destroy Frenchie
and her six helpless children. One day
Frenchie panicked in fear and fled by taxi
to Scotland Yard and begged the police
for constant protection for her family. The
men at the Yard, realising Frenchie's terrible story was no more than a figment of
her wild imagination, saw no alternative
but to return her back to the safety of
Rachel.

Night was the worst for Frenchie, for she
was petrified that the French Algerians would
swarm into the ward through the nearby toilet
window. I suggested that if her fear of the
night became too terrifying for her to bear
she was welcome to stay the night in the
safety of my room, convincing her that they

wouldn't dare attack in front of such a sensible witness as I. Her gratitude filled me with embarrassment, she kissed my hands and face like an over-grateful puppy dog who had just been saved from the vet gas chamber.

I would make Frenchie comfortable in a small armchair beside my bed, wrapping a blanket round her waist, and then sit talking and smoking through the long depressing nights of Frenchie's imagined horror. Many times I would be glad of Night Sister's suggestion that Frenchie should go to her own bed space, in order to let my burning eyes rest.

So demanding was Frenchie's request for my company, I would turn my head away from her pleas of despair, for when Sister took her bodily Frenchie would pull away, sobbing, 'Please, Rosie, don't let them take me, please help me.' There was no way I could help her, there was nothing within my reach that would help ease Frenchie's pain and suffering, nothing except an extra-strong dose of sleepers, or a bottle of real genuine love that she could drink from each time she felt lost and alone.

So different were all our sad tales, yet how similar the medication we longed for. We all knew there was no substitute for love and understanding, you could not acquire it on the National Health, neither could any doctor on earth supply it on prescription.

Christmas was creeping into Rachel with very little enthusiasm, for none of us cared much whether it was Christmas, Easter or the end of the world. We sat at the windows looking down on to the Mile End waste market, where a long trail of wooden stalls stretched along one side of Whitechapel High Street. As energetic shoppers bustled about the street beneath our dreamy gaze, we did not envy or care about their frenzy of rushing, pushing, and occasionally bickering over the price of some insignificant item of high-fashion attire.

The brightly painted stalls were heavy and bursting with the season's collection of gay fruities, rusty red Cox's Pippin apples, sun-kissed tangerines, and large net sacks of different types of hard, shelled nuts.

A host of ragamuffin pigeons wobbled round

the base of a mobile hot-dog stand, cooing and prancing, hoping to reach the hearts of the hungry beefburger-gobblers. Two or three impoverished tramps wandered in and out of the busy crowd which paid no heed to the shabby, string-waisted beggars. The world around me echoed and buzzed with zest and the joys of living, even the poor old tramps were alive, if only to beg.

A one-footed, half-starved pigeon was cooing with happiness as he pecked at the skin of a rotting apple. In the presence of such simple appreciation of life I felt inadequate, abnormal, and disturbingly dead. So completely and in such tender detail did Frenchie and Bones describe the noisy sight beneath the half-open window, I saw half-through my distant memory far more than the loving company at my side did.

God slouched towards us, curious to know what had captured our interested gaze.

'What you looking at?' he asked abruptly, clutching my shoulder like he was trying to crush my bones.

I was half afraid he was about to have one of his crazy outbursts, so I tried to soothe him by asking as politely as possible, 'Hello, God, and how are you today?' I hoped to get a pleasant response which would prove to me that today he might be on the road to recovery.

But God broke my dreams of hope to pieces, as he crudely replied, 'I've been masturbating all morning and trying hard to stick a long pencil up my bum.'

So fed up was I of his verbal sex thing, I lost my sense of reason and angrily replied without thought.

'I'm fucking sick of you playing with yourself. Ain't you got anything better to do? And we are sick of seeing you parading round Rachel in the nude, I wouldn't mind if you had something big to brag about.'

Frenchie interrupted my anger with her question, 'Did the French Algerians tell you to come to my bed last night with nothing on so that you could rape me?'

Bones burst into laughter.

'You know, God, you mustn't go round all the time with no clothes on. After all, it's not a very pretty sight.'

God's blank eyes filled with the moisture of sorrow.

'I'm sorry,' he mumbled, his small head hung forward as he repentantly walked away, still mumbling, 'I'm sorry, I don't want to hurt anyone, for I am God, I love everyone, I'm sorry.'

The following day at the group therapy session, Long Dog set about drawing the man named Empty into her clever trap of making people divulge their past histories, and Empty was easy prey. Empty was a youthful fifty-nine with a full mop of healthy silver hair. He showed no trace of middle-age spread, and his bright way of thinking was not out of step with my own age group. His dark-brown eyes were always so sad, they made you want to cry just looking at him. He gave his everything to the respectful circle of listeners. We learned of how he had married a beautiful homely woman when they were both in their mid-twenties. They were compatible in everything, dancing, travelling, and loving their lives away, for there were no children to interfere with their blissful lives. Empty's wife was unable to conceive, but it never bothered him. As long as he had her, there was little else he wanted.

Happiness ruled the roost in their compact Stepney flatlet, but only for ten years.

Cancer struck Empty's beloved and its savage tentacles tore at her beauty like she was being devoured alive. Empty, for two long, heart-breaking years stood back helpless, watching her turn day by day into a living skeleton. And now, fifteen years after his bereavement, he sat, hunched and defeated, having made an attempt to end his misery by swallowing a huge amount of sleeping tablets. His explanation was that he just wanted to be with his wife.

Long Dog asked him if he now felt lonely.

'No, I'm not lonely,' sighed he. 'There are people all around me, so how can I be lonely? You're only lonely when you are alone.' He swallowed deep as if a stone were stuck in his throat. 'I just feel empty as if someone has cut half of my heart away.'

Tears formed behind my black-windowed spectacles as Empty continued his sad story.

'If only she had left a piece of her behind, a son or a daughter, just something living that actually came from her, I would not feel quite so empty now.'

God, who had sat unusually still listening to Empty's every word, suddenly burst into tears.

'My father died of cancer when I was ten years old, and I watched him die.'

Dr Bright urged him to carry on talking.

'I became a man when I was ten,' sobbed God, wiping his running nose on the cuff of his dressing-gown. 'I was the eldest of five kids and my mum wasn't well enough to cope with us. Has anyone here ever seen a dead person?'

I listened attentively without asking myself where am I. Suddenly I knew I was in a group of society to which I belonged. My never-ending quest to fit in somewhere in this world was at last reached, as though a huge heavy curtain had lifted from my brain. I was overwhelmed by my realisation that I was part of the lost, those rare and wonderful creatures of society who don't belong.

But we are here to be made better, to be able to keep in tune with the rest of the world – how do we get better, and what does getting better mean? How do you train yourself not to weep at death, not to crumble inside when witnessing extreme cruelty and suffering? How does Empty stop aching and how can God stop hurting because of cruel circumstances?

The strange dawning of my true self filled me with added sorrow, for today I had become over-sensitively aware of the fact that there was little hope of my getting better. After hearing of God's childhood experience, my mind rushed back to when I was ten.

The sun was streaming into the parlour of my two-up, two-down tiny house at Stratford in the East End of London. The sun hung around my father's great polished coffin, its brilliant rays danced upon the cold brass coffin-bearer's handles, making them come alive with dazzling, eye-blinding sparks of brightness.

I prayed to the sun, please, and God, please, let the sun warm my father's body back to life, for he is the only one with whom I can communicate.

'Kiss him,' demanded my mother, pushing my trembling little head into the smelly depths of my beloved father's cold tomb.

My sobbing lips pressed on to damp dead flesh – I screamed, for my own very dear father filled me with revulsion. I imagined how much I must have hurt Dad by my display of fear and disgust, but I loved him alive when he was warm and loving. I tried to tell God of my guilt, and begged His forgiveness, but God didn't answer, He left my guilt within me, like a black canyon of emptiness.

Lucy brought me back to the world of today, with her half-screaming, half-singing voice. She was leaning over my person looking directly into my eyes.

'I beg your pardon, I never promised you a rose garden.'

Her bottom was covered in an extremely tight pair of heavy-stitched jeans. Lucy was bent over me with her wobbling backside protruding in straight view of shy Dr Scramble. As Lucy sang, her bottom wagged seductively. Once again, Lucy had handed me a plateful of laughter, just when I needed it most. I'm almost certain Lucy's timing was cleverly planned. For each time I found myself sinking into a deep pool of sadness, up she would pop, like a well-trained clown, to make my inside ripple with the wonderful glow of comedy.

Long Dog suggested to 'Singing Lucy' that she should leave the group and continue her theatrical display in the solitude of her own room, so that the other patients could sensibly discuss their problems. Lucy reluctantly obeyed Long Dog's command.

No one ever talked to Lucy apart from myself. If she entered the day room or kitchen, the occupants would disappear. It puzzled me for I saw nothing in Lucy's nature to be afraid of. Lucy and I would frequently stroll along the soft corridor leading away from Rachel and down two flights of winding stairs ending in the basement, where lay the bright hospital shop, which sold everything from strawberry jam to seamless tights. Because I could not see, I was spared the sight of the porters' mocking faces, for Lucy, on our daily travels, would broadcast to every passing face that we were the residents of the crazy ward. People avoided Lucy and me like we were victims of a bubonic plague, and yet it never really bothered me, for I too remember the stigma I placed on to Rachel

Ward. I had even warned Mark and Sarah to keep well clear of Rachel, because it was full of weird, mad people who were not to be trusted at any price, but that was a long time ago, long before I had been educated about all the true details of mental illness.

Lucy and I were good for each other and I am sure our doctors realised this. Me with my disgust with society, believing the world to be a stinking pisshole of a place, and Lucy trying her utmost to make me believe everything and everyone to be all sweet and beautiful. I had to chastise her constantly for being far too friendly and affectionate towards strangers. I tried to explain that she must not greet cleaners, porters and laundry staff with a kiss, because it gave the wrong impression.

'But I love people,' Lucy would say, smiling with warmth and love.

I in turn helped her overcome her childish unreasonable behaviour, for when Lucy led me to the shop she had to be in command, and my whole well-being was left in her care. Lucy had to behave like a sensible adult, for the ward sister had made her entirely responsible for another patient.

But, oh dear me, did we land up in terrible trouble on all too many occasions. Like once Lucy got an idea into her head which I also thought was a brilliant suggestion. We both decided to give some of our useless time to the poor hospital children, who might be glad of our happy singing personalities. Lucy and stumbling me got completely lost in the maze of push-button lifts and passageways. We ended up in a ward full of men with plastered arms, legs and things, I am not sure how it all came about. Lovely Lucy was giving them a real good imitation of Shirley Temple and the good ship Lollypop while I sat comforting a worried old man about to experience his first operation.

Our captive audience was showing its fond appreciation by rocking the high-sprung beds with roars of infectious laughter, until a stern, mannish ward sister entered the room so full of unexpected happiness. She crossly demanded to know from where giggling Lucy and I had come. Innocently Lucy announced we had skipped out of Rachel. The angry sister turned on us like we were a pair of foolish freaks from outer space.

'Out, out,' she growled, pushing my retreating body, for she didn't know I was half-blind.

I must have given her the impression that I was some sort of half-brained, stumbling moron, for I was staggering along the safety of the walls, touching trolleys and medicine cabinets, passing nurses and door handles, as if I were a groping maniac. I know I should have tried to explain, but the opportunity never came, because Lucy was in full verbal battle with the over-excited sister. Lucy's last words made even the bewildered, less-important staff smile.

'Oh shit!' yelled Lucy, spraying the vexed sister's red face with a fine instant shower of mouth moisture, 'we have been thrown out of better places than this.' Lucy linked my arm into hers and gave me a nudge of confirmation. 'Ain't we, Stumbles?'

I nodded my mystified head, everything was happening too fast for me. In any case, my moral support wasn't really needed, for Lucy was more than capable of handling any embarrassing situation, because by now she was hardened to almost anything.

Our secret escapades of confusing adventure reached their climax on the day Lucy led me to the other side of our institution of fun and fancy. I unexpectedly found myself inside the forbidden walls of the doctors' dining-room, where loving Lucy was busy chatting up every good-looking specimen of male in sight, whether he was a registrar, scientific genius or professor. Within fifteen minutes, Rachel Ward was telephoned.

Nurse Sue, who was standing in for Sister, ushered us back to Rachel, nagging us all the way from the doctors' dining-room along the winding corridors and stairs. Sue was furious, she kept wagging her angry tongue and pointing her finger at us, in funny sudden outbursts. Sue would be quiet for a few moments, walking heavy and swift under a steaming cover of frustration, then without any warning she would stop dead in her tracks, and begin chastising us again and again.

'This is the last straw with you two. I am sick of people calling up Rachel with complaints. For God's sake, can't you try and behave like responsible people. We give you an inch but you always take a yard.'

113

Lucy and I by the end of the day were sick with everyone having a right bad go at us. We both agreed to keep our impulsive behaviour inside the safe grounds of Rachel, or at least we would most certainly try.

It was made very obvious that Lucy was starving. All she wanted was to be loved. Like me, she was born and raised in an environment of suppressed feelings, where if you gave the impression of being soft and sensitive it was frowned upon as a sign of weakness. We were taught at an early age to fight and fend for ourselves – if you cried you got a beating for displaying such meekness to the waiting back-street enemy. As far back as I can remember, I can't recall my mother ever kissing me good-night. You had to lick your wounds in silence and condition yourself into accepting violence as a necessary part of normal life. How much villainy and skullduggery must Lucy have experienced to make her crack quicker than I? No, I was the one who cracked, for Lucy didn't really crack, she just bloody crumbled.

CHAPTER NINE

It was now only two days away from Christmas Eve, and my most favourite time of the day, which was lovely, scrumptious, early-morning breakfast. Most of the sleepy patients did not rise till somewhere after nine. Only four or five of us appeared at the dining-room each morning for the normal routine eight o'clock breakfast. There were two large round Formica-topped tables in the dining-room, bright flowery curtains hung down each side of two long spacious windows. The smallness of the place made you feel very cosy and warm inside. At other mealtimes two nurses stood at the back of two hot mobile food trolleys and the patients queued in good-mannered rotation while the nurses dished out the choice of food. But at breakfast there were no staff at all – the patients just helped themselves.

My morning company was always Frenchie, Empty, sometimes Lucy, and always soft sensitive Bones. I sat like a queen at a table of loyal subjects, who hovered and waited on my every whim. Never in all my existence had I indulged in such extreme comfort. Because of my failing eyesight I was fussed over with bowls of thick, rather watery porridge, razor-thin slices of tempting bacon, diabetic marmalade and countless cups of good strong hot tea, most of which was tenderly placed in front of me by beautifully timid Bones.

Just think, if I could see at this very moment, where would I otherwise be? Working my guts out, I suppose – I would be frantically rushing round my tiny council kitchen, hurrying Mark and Sarah up, making sure they had their school lunch money, which more than likely I would have run round the night before for trying to borrow it off some half-broke neighbour. Then off to work in some grotty pub full of out-of-work depressives trying to drink their troubles away. But because today I am nearly blind, I can't work, I can't join the mad rushing crowd of money-worshippers. I am here, for the first time in my life, being waited on hand and foot. If there is some kind of superior being watching our every move, then he must certainly like me.

'Have you had enough ham, Rosie?' smiled Bones, removing my dirty breakfast plate.

I assured him that I was satisfied. Without asking, Bones refilled my empty tea cup, for he knew it was usual for me to down four cups in the early morning. On some days we would sit and talk at the breakfast table for two happy hours. Bones was a Japanese-American who had left his homeland six months earlier because he said the pace of living was too fast. He thought he might find more peace of mind if he travelled to England, and he began working in some secluded country town way up in the hilly countryside of Green Wales.

Bones was an extremely well-educated and very bright orthopaedic doctor, full of modesty and great understanding. When we talked together I felt as though he were reading me like an open book. Bones instinctively knew my every mood. When I was low he would come to my room and invite me out to a local pub, which he knew would cheer me up, and when I was too high for my own good Bones could bring me back down to ground-level without my being aware of his clever psychology.

His own eyesight was very poor, and he had to wear very thick-lensed spectacles in order to read properly. Slightly bandy-legged, he walked from his hips, keeping the top half of his very small-boned body rigid and upright. There was little about his appearance to cause any normal woman pangs of passion: he had plain flat features and undisciplined cross-over teeth. In his early thirties and six years younger than I, Bones was dead and hollow, even more so than myself.

Frenchie left the table, saying she must phone her husband to make sure the children were safe. We all tried to persuade her not to bother her husband, as her constant phone calls were annoying both him and her frightened children. But Frenchie, obsessed with the thought of the Algerians kidnapping her innocent children, fled from the table in panic towards the wall phone just outside my room.

Empty was so sad and depressed that morning he also retreated from our company saying he wanted to lie on his bed and have a think about his morbid future, leaving Bones and me to finish off the half-empty pot of cooling tea.

Bones gave me a cigarette, looked at me with puzzlement and softly asked, 'Rosie, why are you in this place? You seem so intelligent and bright.'

I puffed on my cigarette and blew the smoke from the corner of my mouth.

'I don't like living very much, Bones, I'm suicidal.'

Bones pulled his flat head back, shocked at my reply.

'But you have a family, Rosie.'

I shrugged.

'So what.'

I didn't have to say any more because as usual Bones knew my inner thoughts of loneliness. No matter how many people were involved in my home life, I could still feel alone. Bones sat silently watching me, waiting for my story to flow free from my smoky lips without any form of pressure put upon me by run-of-the-mill questions. I gave a long deep sigh of boredom.

'I took an overdose of sleepers and I almost cracked it, perhaps next time I'll do better.'

I don't know if Bones was testing my passion for death, but his unusual comment made me screw up tight inside.

'You shouldn't try sleepers, Rosie, the success rate is not very high, you know.'

Bones slowly filled our cups with fresh milk and tea and carried on talking lazily about the pitfalls of suicide, how it often failed.

'There's only one way to go and there's no way you can turn back and change your mind once you've done it, it's a hundred per cent foolproof.'

I sat, fascinated by his casual manner when talking about such a delicate subject, for at home I was never allowed to mention such an evil word as suicide, no one ever asked why I wanted to die, they just said I was wicked and bad not wanting to exist any more.

'The only thing to do, Rosie – that's if

you're set on the idea of suicide.' Bones smiled and gazed into my very soul, it made me shudder with exposure. 'You get in a car and drive to the tallest mountain and over the top, there's no turning back.'

Bones flopped his head forward and turned his small palms face-upwards on the shiny table, like he had just given away his most cherished secret in life. I just had to ask him.

'Do you like living, Bones?'

He gave a hopeless chuckle and I knew I had played the wrong key.

'No, Rosie, I am not suicidal, I like life.'

I impulsively asked, 'Why are you here then?'

Bones fumbled and fussed with a grubby matchstick, he began drawing tiny patterns with the fine layer of grey dust lying in our tin ashtray, like a bored little boy at the seaside. Bones sighed and swayed his downcast head slowly from side to side.

'You see, Rosie, my trouble is that I don't like myself, I have no respect for my own being.'

'I don't believe it,' snapped I like an over-protective mother, 'Bones, you're beautiful inside.'

Tears danced in his eyes like blobs of cold glass behind the extra-thick lenses of his spectacles.

'It's mighty nice of you to say that, Rosie, but you are a romantic fool.' He grabbed hold of my hand, afraid his thoughtless words had hurt me. Bones stuttered nervously, trying to make amends. 'It's nice to be the way you are, Rosie. But I can be real mean at times, you see, I use people to get what I want from life.'

Five energetic young nurses bounced into the dining-room, chatting and laughing about some unusual event that had tickled their comedy buds the night before. With regimental zest they quickly cleared our dirty crockery on to the food trolley.

Bones' sincerity changed. He suddenly became slick and cunning, throwing untrue compliments at the impressed nurses, who bathed in his sweet-sounding comments like childish nymphs exhilarated by the fountain of youth.

I stared at Bones with a spark of honest jealousy shining within my misty eyes, and I knew not why, after the host of high-spirited nurses left our company, I snapped at Bones, revealing the not-so-nice side of my loving nature.

'Why do you talk like that?'

Bones' yellowy skin reddened.

'What do you mean, Rosie?'

I felt like I wanted to be truthfully nasty.

'The way you throw silly compliments around Rachel like a shower of plastic confetti.'

Bones asked me the true reason lying behind my angry attitude, for he knew me better than I knew my own self.

I tried to explain my inner feelings as simply as I could.

'Well,' said I, turning my gaze towards the long rainy window at my side, 'you seem to give everyone in this place compliments, the nurses, the patients, even the bloody snooty doctors, everyone, except me.'

Bones handed me another cigarette, which gave him time to sort out a good reply.

'Well, it's just that you don't seem to need any compliments.'

'You must be joking,' laughed I in pretence, 'I don't even know what I look like, there is no mirror for me, I don't know whether or not I look a complete mess or if I am covered in spots and wrinkles, I don't even know when my clothes are dirty.'

Bones tenderly pulled my turned profile towards his.

'Rosie, I can't pay you any compliments because if I did I would be using you to get something back, and I don't want to do that. I am paying you a great honour, because you are the first one I've met I don't want to crawl round with sweet false words in order to play on your silly vanity. In any case, Rosie, I've never really seen you give me any signs of no confidence.'

I felt like screaming at his acute observation of self-made confidence.

'You bloody idiot, Bones, of course I don't get embarrassed like any other normal person. I could stand in full view of a million eyes and talk my head off, but that's only because I can't see them.'

Bones touched a long thick strand of my hair which was lying over my shoulder.

'Don't you think that makes you a very lucky person, Rosie?'

I was rather annoyed when Dr Bright interrupted our intimate conversation by telling me she would like to talk with me in the privacy of her office. She held my hand and led me along the carpeted hallway to her personal talking-room. She gave me a comfortable chair and conveniently placed a heavy glass ashtray by my right hand. Dr Bright slid back into her roomy chair giving herself an air of extreme relaxation.

'Now then, Rosie, how do you feel?'

I was so mixed up inside I didn't really know how I felt.

'I don't think the tablets you are giving me are much good.'

Dr Bright agreed with my diagnosis, saying she would from today double the dosage from three to six daily. Dr Bright's reason for the interview was to find out a little more about my past history.

I began with the sad death of my father, and went on to when I was eleven years old, when my whole family was thrown out of our house by the dreaded bailiff, because my impoverished mother could not pay the rent. After this distressing event I lost all trace of my brothers and sister for they all married in haste so that they could put their roots of life into a secure dwelling of their own. I stayed with mother being as I was the youngest. Mum and I lived in a poxy, rat-infested room where huge ugly cockroaches gobbled at our clothing like tiny black creatures of the devil's making. At seventeen I married the first man who paid me attention. We lived with my mother who by now had stepped up in life, for the local council had given her a three-roomed, mice-ridden upstairs flat, with a toilet stuck way outside in the grubby back yard. Nothing would induce me to climb down the creaking stairs and into the yard full of hungry stray cats in the dead of night when I wanted to go to the toilet. So a plastic bucket was used for the purpose and each morning it was slops out for most of the neighbourhood.

After a few fruitless years of wasted energy I gave birth to my beautiful son Mark, after spending five tedious months inside the

London Hospital. Eighteen months later Jim and I were allocated a two-bedroom council flat. My mother married a kind elderly man who she had met in the canteen of the East India Docks where she was working as an early-morning breakfast cook.

Sarah was born two and a half years after Mark. With such a complete family unit, life should have been blissfully perfect. But my only way of describing married life would be for me to say it was absolutely soul-destroying in every way, for by the time little Sarah was three years old, I had no religion, no faith or hope in anything except the ugly facts of human survival. Jim turned his selfish back, leaving me to cope alone with all the responsibilities of running a home and family. His meanness with money was indescribable, for he gave me a weekly allowance of £10 to feed and clothe our family, plus I had the extra worry of weekly hire purchase debts. In order to survive I dabbled in everything and anything – shoplifting, the selling of stolen property – while Jim got more fat and content with every passing day, spending the remainder of his vast income on drink and fine Indian suppers. Alcohol was as necessary to his being as sunshine and rain were to a willow tree. Through his constant explosions of drunken brutality I became the perfect example of a hopeless battered wife. Many times I ran helplessly away and there were always sympathetic places for me to hide. But I always went back home for wherever I stayed I had the terrifying feeling of not belonging, like I once felt long ago when I was a child, thrown into the cold street, like an unwanted puppy dog.

After many long dragging years of pleading and arguing Jim reluctantly raised my weekly allowance up to the grateful sum of £15, but with the growing prices I found his generosity useless. It wasn't until my eyes began crying blood that I simply had to give up my working days.

I told Dr Bright that until the time came to convince me there was something good in living, and there really were people in this world who cared, I would stick with my belief that the world was no more than a great big greedy pisshole. I wanted to tell her that if she had not interrupted Bones and me at breakfast, he might have succeeded in brainwashing me into thinking otherwise.

To prove normality it was expected of you to ask permission to return back home for the Christmas festivities. My request was granted although I was only half-hearted about the issue. Whether it was my imagination, I know not, but when I returned home to my family they seemed hostile towards my presence. I remember very little about Christmas, I know I slept quite a lot and ate very little. I can't remember if anyone talked to me, for if they did it must have been of little importance, for at the time all I wanted to do was to get back to my friends in Rachel, I missed them so much it hurt.

CHAPTER TEN

My first day back in Rachel was gloriously warm and wonderful, we were all gasping with relief, greeting one another with kisses of inner happiness. Poor Frenchie had been dragged back early Christmas morning by her hard-hearted husband, leaving her sobbing on to Bones' shoulder, who was the only one left in the ward over Christmas. Empty had stayed with his brother's family, which for Empty could have been on a lonely desert island for all he knew. Lucy was allowed home daily, her devoted parents returned her each evening.

Night crept about Whitechapel, wielding a fine metallic paintbrush in its artistic hand, the streets beneath us were streaked glistening white. The local gathering of frozen beggars sniffed and cuffed at their bright-red noses, like out-of-work circus clowns. The tall hard structure of the hospital was softened here and there with lines of delicate silver. The few trees left standing along the pavements were leafless and silent, while Mr Frost played tormenting havoc with their undefended branches.

The night outside was bitterly cold, but I was warm and secure. I lay on my bed wondering how many homeless tramps would gladly trade places with me at this very moment. I gazed up on to the still, white ceiling.

'Oh fuck,' I mumbled, 'my eyes are crying blood again.'

Running slowly across my sight were great streaky red tears of blood. How I hated it, for I felt as though I had used all my real tears up and was now down to straining my raw blood, as though I were dried up of the real weeping moisture, which any other normal person possesses.

I lay thinking of Dr Bright's persistence in telling me I was born to write. I thought: How stupid, for how can you write without eyes?

I could feel Dr Bright's seeds of inspiration taking root inside my head, their growth was pushing my thoughts of death into a corner of my brain. I kept repeating her words to my inner thoughts.

Rosie, have you thought about the thousands of diabetics who have suffered in the same way as you, you have the gift that will enable you to write about it, so why don't you try and help these people who have not got your talent and what of those who suffer from mental breakdowns? Think about it, Rosie, you just think about it.

'Can I join you, Rosie?' called a short shadow standing inside my open door. 'It's me, Bones.'

'Of course, come in,' beckoned I, swinging upwards on my bed and tucking my feet beneath my body.

Bones told me that Lucy and Frenchie had been given a good measure of sleeping draught by the night staff.

'I wondered why the place was quiet tonight,' grinned I.

Bones pulled over the small, green-wheeled armchair beside my bed.

'Fancy a nice pot of tea?' said Bones. 'I'll go and make some if you like.'

A proper little scivvy he was to me and I loved it, for it was such a rare thing for me to be waited upon by a man, especially by someone as clever as an orthopaedic surgeon. Bones left and returned ten minutes later carrying a tray of hot tea and toast. He spoke apologetically.

'Sorry, it's only toast for supper tonight, Rosie, but it's a bit too late for Chinese or Indian.'

Most nights Bones and Empty would treat us all to a Chinese or Indian take-away supper, which we would sit and talk over in the day room till twelve o'clock at night. It gave me great cause for concern, because of Bones' shabby attire. I thought it too much strain on his low financial pocket.

'Bones, you must stop spending all your money on those very expensive suppers.'

He laughed at my motherly concern.

'Rosie, I must tell you, I am a very rich guy, with about seventy thousand dollars in the bank back home.'

I opened my eyes wide with amazement at his extremely modest ways.

'Blimey, why ain't you happy with all that kind of bread? You can do anything.'

Bones shrugged his thin shoulders with total lack of interest.

'What good is all my money if I have no peace of mind? I keep telling you, Rosie, I am not a very nice guy, I always get what I want and I don't deserve it.'

'Have you ever thought of getting married, Bones?'

Bones sucked on the side of his mouth and replied, 'Yep, I've thought about it but I'd never do it, because I know it would never work out, I am so mean I would destroy my wife.'

Bones carried on talking for the next two hours. He told me he was born in an internment camp because during the Second World War all the Jap families were rounded up inside America and placed into camps. After the war Bones travelled half-way across the States with his elder brother and parents, and one hundred dollars tucked inside his back pocket, which at the time was all his family's worldly possessions. Within ten years his ambitious father owned four blocks of tenement flats, and today he is retired with a beautiful expensive house, with outside patio and swimming pool.

The longer Bones talked the wider the gap came between us. When he talked of money it was like telephone numbers. When I spoke on the subject, it was one pound-note at a time. How foolish I felt, thinking of how I had pitied Bones and shared half of my fruit with him, when he could have probably bought the whole blinking stallful. His talk of fine beautiful possessions made me feel very sorry for him, so I kept his secret wealth to myself, just in case the people around him became more dazzled by his surface wealth than by his true inner value.

I gave Bones a cigarette and offered him one of my sweet tangerines, which he never ever refused. We always tried to skin the orange fruit without separating any piece of the skin. Bones' nimble fingers released the fruit inside without distorting the outer peel. He turned the empty skin upside-down in his juicy palm to make it look like the tangerine had never been peeled by human hands.

'There,' smiled Bones, 'absolutely perfect.'

He beamed with satisfaction like he had just performed some brilliant, successful operation. What a damn pity he owned so much, yet had so little. How on earth can some coppy little brainless tangerine give someone so much pleasure?

It was two o'clock in the morning when Bones said good-night and lazily retired to his bed unit. I lay listening to Lonely sobbing softly into her pillow, her weeping was common to my ears now, so I didn't dwell too long on her suffering before dropping off into my deep slumber.

A few hours later I was woken by Peter, a tall, fair, handsome male nurse who urgently requested a specimen of my urine, after which he very gently gave me my daily jab of insulin. My skin was beginning to feel as tough as a rhinoceros's, for after thousands of days of routine injections I could feel the texture of it changing. I was very happy to be born a woman for at least I had soft convenient pockets of fat spread evenly around my belly and thighs.

But what of the male diabetic, whose body is already tough, made up of nothing but hard muscle and sinews, ouch, I wonder how many steel hypodermic needles bend or break in the process of supplying his body with the life-saving insulin.

After a delightful breakfast with Frenchie, Empty and Bones, I bathed and washed my hair, not out of necessity but more through boredom. Long Dog was on the prowl, gathering up her slow subjects in preparation for the eleven o'clock group discussion.

The circle was made up of its usual constituency of half-introverts, half-extroverts. The introverts were all young, ranging from fifteen to early-twenties, all suffering from the common complaint – the only way I can describe it is to call it zombiemania. These dull, sullen-mouthed young people never laughed, cried, talked or lost their temper, no matter how hard Long Dog provoked them. The sad victims of zombiemania passed through Rachel like a swarm of half-dead bees searching for the sweet taste of life, giving honey only to be discharged with their hungry insides still on the cruel border of starvation. I found I couldn't help but think of this unhappy breed of dissatisfied people as revolutionaries, backing away from modern society in the only way they subconsciously knew how. I feared my lovely sensitive Sarah might soon join the company of the zombiemaniacs. Lonely, a girl of twenty-four, acted as spokesman for the whole group. She addressed Long Dog with an air of cool control.

'I think it's about time something was done about Lucy.'

'I agree,' shouted an angry young man. 'Lucy woke me up at six o'clock this morning asking me if I was Rock Hudson.'

Long Dog replied in defence of absent Lucy.

'But Lucy's not well, and we should all try and make allowances for her strange behaviour.' Long Dog looked the angry young man straight in the eyes. 'Are you forgetting, David, that there was a time when you thought you were Harold Wilson, and you wanted to change the world?'

An over-vexed woman called out in defence of David, 'Yes, but David was never as crazy as Lucy.'

All of a sudden loud voices jumped from every part of the noisy circle.

'I think Lucy should be locked up with another lot of mad Lucys,' and other comments such as, 'Lucy has no right to be in Rachel, she's crazy, I think she should be put away in an asylum.'

Up to today I had said very little in the group, except for the occasional yes or no. But right now I wanted to shout my head off at the wild pack of persecutors demanding Lucy's crazy hide.

Dr Bright as cool as ice-cream gazed all round the ring of agitated faces and calmly asked, 'Is there anyone in this group who is not afraid of Lucy's wild behaviour?'

I could stand it no longer, I jumped to my feet like an untrained jack-in-a-box. I shouted at the group in mad fury.

'I am more afraid of you stinking lot of selfish bastards than I am of Lucy. What, if I got as ill as her I'd be terrified to think you would all persecute me like you are doing right this moment with Lucy. At least she laughs, she cries, she dances and sings, not like you lot of fucking deadpan zombies.'

Everyone was staring at my blast of passionate verbal. Their speechless mouths hung open like stunned mackerels on a fishmonger's marble slab. I had the floor and was going to have their full attention, for I was determined to say my piece at all costs.

'Does anyone ever take the trouble to go to Lucy's room to see if she's happy or if she needs help to dress herself? No, of course you don't, because you are all too wrapped up in your bloody selves.'

I felt like I was talking to a hard brick wall with each person one single brick, yet all stuck together to form a huge solid wall, which I just could not break through.

'Oh, balls to the lot of you.'

I turned and stomped away, tripping head-over-heels over a short coffee table. I picked myself up in temper and hastily retreated to my room. I threw myself on to my bed and listened. The distant group was silent for a good ten minutes, then voices began to talk softly, too faint for my strained ear to understand. Fifteen minutes later I heard the gathering disperse for twelve o'clock lunch.

Well, Rosie, thought I, you've done it all wrong again, opened your big stupid mouth without thinking. I must try to stop swearing, but I only swear when I am angry, and I don't know what I am saying when I am angry. I tutted with disgust at myself. I suppose no one will talk to me now, I'm gonna be a loner once again.

'Your dinner's waiting for you, Rosie,' said Bones as he swayed into my room.

Frightening thoughts ran across my mind. How can I go down to the packed dining-room and face all those people, who I have just insulted so badly? I reckon they will all turn their disgusted backs on me. Oh no, I just can't face them.

Bones pulled gently on my hand.

'Come on, Rosie, I'll take you, your dinner's getting cold.'

He tried to steer me off my bed, but I pulled away from his friendly grip.

'I can't, Bones, I just can't face them, not after my terrible display of bad manners.'

Bones grabbed my hand again, squeezing it tightly.

'Gee, Rosie, you were great.' Bones giggled

like a naughty child. 'It was the damn best group meeting we have ever had.' He tugged me away from the safety of my bed. 'Do you know what Lonely's doing right this moment, she's washing Lucy's hair and fussing over her like she was her mother. Ain't that swell?'

Then Squirrel entered, came towards me, and clumsily stuck a shaking cup and saucer in my hand.

Squirrel was an ex-school mistress suffering from loss of memory. Just like a tiny little creature who's storing his winter nuts, she hid her personal belongings, but in such perculiar places she could never remember where. In her early sixties, she had the charming mannerisms of a shy little girl full of innocent curiosity. Squirrel smiled affectionately.

'I brought you a nice cup of tea, Rosie, and after lunch I'll wash your hair for you.' Squirrel then stopped unexpectedly, stopped short in the middle of her sentence, and tapped her frowned temple with her finger, as if just remembering where she had misplaced her mind. 'Ah yes, I remember, won't be long,' and off she shuffled, mumbling something regarding a pair of pink bloomers to her forgetful self.

Bones shook his head and remarked, 'Same old Squirrel,' then returned back to the theme of today's group therapy.

It made me feel real good inside when Bones said he thought me to be great. But his next sentence made me float even higher.

'You know what happened today, Rosie?'

I nodded my head vaguely for I didn't really know what he was suggesting.

Bones patted me heartily on my bony back.

'You came alive, Rosie, you showed for the very first time since I've known you real anger, spirit, passion and love for Lucy.'

Bones is right, I am not empty inside, I am bursting bloody full.

The rest of the day Lucy and I were the centre of attraction. The other female patients dressed and undressed her, combed her hair, powdered her face and absolutely pampered and petted her like a playful kitten and Lucy loved every affectionate moment. How elegantly smart she looked and what a wonderful transformation since only yesterday, when singing Lucy waltzed round Rachel trying to draw attention, by dressing herself in four inside-out, back-to-front sweaters, a pair of tight jeans plus thick, bright-green corduroy skirt, two floppy hats, and worst of all a pair of long white fluffy sanitary towels looped over her pretty pink ears, which Lucy insisted were the latest fashion in ear jewellery.

The nursing staff were all patient, well trained, and understanding towards Lucy's wearing nature, but there was one very important thing missing for her, which was the help of only one good honest friend. All you needed in times of stress and trouble was someone you could trust and rely on completely, one who wholeheartedly cared about your true being.

My own recovery was being made a great deal easier, for I was lucky in respect of having one good friend, in the vivacious shape of the publican Jenny, whose equally sincere husband was the hard-grafting landlord of a small, elegantly furnished public house, lying on the corner of Hoxton Market.

Jack and Jenny of the White Hart had deliberately chosen each minute piece of pub furnishing with extreme loving care, and their place of income reflected their love of a time when people took pleasure and pride in carving wood and moulding brass and copper.

Each week without fail Jenny visited Rachel giving me two or three hours of her limited time. Although Jenny's bubbling personality was somewhat overbearing at times, beneath her impulsive, non-stop chatter lay a kind, loving soul, who found extreme inner happiness when given the chance to give a kind helping hand to others less fortunate than her wealthy self.

CHAPTER ELEVEN

'Why don't you use this? said Bones, straightening my white collapsible walking stick.

How I loathed its presence in my hand.

'I'll never use it,' scowled I in contempt.

Bones broke the thin stick into four short pieces, then slotted them all back together again by its automatic spring.

'You know, Rosie, the guy who designed this must have been pretty bright.' Bones pushed the stick into my hostile hand.

I threw it on to my bed, and snapped at him, 'Would you wear a big badge saying mental nutcase?'

'It could help you, Rosie.'

Bones' persistence was beginning to annoy me, and he could feel it in my sharp reply.

'What, help me to get more pity?'

Bones took the stick from my bed, collapsing it into the neat compact plastic cover.

'It could fit quite easily into a handbag or a man's pocket.'

I had to laugh.

'Don't try your crafty bullshit on me, Bones, I am a bit too shrewd for your game.'

I was growing a little suspicious of Bones, thinking he and Dr Bright were in some sort of conspiracy together, hoping to brainwash me into using that dreadful identification stick of the helpless.

Bones asked if I had been introduced to the new patient named Oliver. Bones seemed very impressed by the fact that Oliver was educated at Eton College, and thought I would be equally delighted about Oliver's high intelligence.

'This is Rosie,' said Bones to the slender young man sprawled in an easy chair in the day room.

His long legs were stretched out rigid in resting abuse on a short polished coffee table. Without stirring he offered me his pale clammy hand.

'Extremely nice to meet you, I'm Oliver.'

It wasn't very often I took an instant dislike to anyone, but Oliver brought a very shuddering feeling back to me as I shook his feeble hand in acknowledgement of our meeting. It was eleven-fifteen in the evening and Oliver was commanding the obedience of all present.

'I say, Rose,' grinned Oliver, 'would you make me a coffee, two sugars, please.'

Lonely, who was sitting next to me, interrupted Oliver's bad-mannered request by reminding him of the fact that my eyes were too dim to chance messing about with the red-hot temperamental kitchen boiler.

I sat trying to put my finger on who sickly Oliver reminded me of.

'I say, could someone turn the TV over to BBC?'

Oliver sat puffing smoke out of his thin tight lips, looking as if he had just popped out of a post-war Noel Coward film. No other person existed in the world except over-demanding Oliver. There seemed in his isolated mind a strange enjoyment of loneliness. People were about his presence merely to cater to his whims of self-satisfaction. I knew the greedy actions of his awful nature were only the symptoms of some terrible mental sickness, but I found great difficulty in conjuring up any true feeling of compassion for his mental disorder. He tore at my nerve-strings and memory-valves, making me feel both distressed and afraid. Each time Oliver opened his powerful mouth I trembled inside. In the hour or so spent in his company I must have nervously smoked at least ten cigarettes, so much for Bones' earlier comment of how well I was progressing. I was coming back to life, he had said, yet at this very moment I was panicking with fear, with unexplained apprehension about just being alive.

I scurried off to the safety of my bed where I could lie undisturbed, tossing questions around my brain like some weird puzzle hoping to fit all my mixed, undisciplined thoughts together. Thinking how wonderful life would be if it were only possible to come up with a beautiful picture of a bright, rosy future.

After two hours of uninterrupted thinking my room gradually grew full of smoke, empty tea cups, filled ashtrays, created by the gossiping company of Empty, Frenchie, laughing Lucy and insomniac Bones, each one revealing their past lives of unsolved riddles and complications. We sat in frustrated puzzlement at the vast universe into which we were thrown. We all agreed that there was a reason for existence, and the only answer was to be found within yourself. The path was there waiting in readiness for our first step, but before that we had to seek out the right road, the one that would eventually lead us onwards to the wonderful domain of peace and inner happiness.

My personal solution was that we earthly mortals were made up of the givers and the takers, and if you gave and took in sane, equal portions then the scales of life would balance in happy perfection. My listeners and I were givers, giving and giving to such stupid excess that we sadly became empty and hollow, with nothing left to give, no tears, no laughter, nothing. On the other hand it could be far more frightening to be classified as a taker, such as Hitler and many more fallen gluttons of history. As far back as the vast

Roman Empire, when man drained his fellow beings until the ravenous grasper of human rights and dignity became so gluttonous he eventually burst at the seams, destroying himself in the unhappy process of always taking.

'Well, I am definitely a giver,' interrupted Empty, full of pride.

Bones slid from my room like a shameful child who had just devoured his younger brother's tiny morsel of cake. Bones' hurt reaction to Empty's genuine remark immediately told me which category of human behaviour he thought himself to fit.

Frenchie sat motionless, gazing out of my window into the blackness of night, her glassy eyes blank and vacant as the cold dull moon above. Her expressionless face did not alter as Frenchie's mouth flapped open and shut like a ventriloquist's upright dummy.

'I don't like being a giver.'

Empty spun his head round as if wondering where the soft timid voice had suddenly flowed from. Frenchie's rigid profile still didn't alter as she carried on talking. Her distant tones sounded more and more like the strictly trained voice of a television news announcer.

'I never stopped giving my husband love, but now he wants me locked away, away in a terrible asylum so that his young mistress can move into my home and take my children from me.'

Empty made a great deal of fuss over a tiny whisp of fluff that had probably been clinging on to his grey, pinstriped trousers all day long. Noticeably trying to avoid Frenchie's disturbingly dead gaze, he tried to give comfort by gently speaking.

'It's like Rosie was just saying, Frenchie, at times one can give too much. Perhaps you suffocated your husband with too much love, it does happen, you know.'

Frenchie jerked her head towards my bed on which I was lazily sprawled.

'But I love him and I don't want to live without him, I'll even share him with this horrible girl.'

Lucy had fallen asleep in the narrow easy chair over by the window, her chubby arm resting against the hard white wash basin like a long uncomfortable pillow. Lucy began snorting like a drugged baby piglet. I spoke loud, and, through Lucy's unconscious gurgling, determined.

'Now, that's crazy talk, Frenchie, you're talking about your husband as though he were a possession. You can't share people like you do your cigarette lighter.'

'But I love him,' insisted Frenchie with as much passion as a dead goldfish.

Empty threw his philosophy into our fruitless conversation.

'Frenchie, can't you realise that your husband most probably doesn't want to be shared like a bloody love machine?'

Sad deprived Frenchie had painfully given birth to six healthy children, giving them her love, time and whole attention, and now her taking husband had cast Frenchie aside, like an ageing used slave. Never did he pay crumbling Frenchie a visit or a few shillings to help her keep her fast-failing pride. Poor Frenchie was wholly dependent on the generous nature of the other patients, who kindly kept her supplied with cigarettes, shampoo, and all the little necessities of daily living.

I see little hope of Frenchie ever finding a successful remedy for her mental disability, for she has no friends, no caring family or loved ones to help her along the dark empty tunnel of loneliness.

Long after Frenchie and Empty had retired to the welcoming world of silent dreams and fantasy, I found myself being beautifully entertained by Nurse Sue and Bones, who had invited me into Sister's small cluttered office. Sue had lent me a book of collected poems, written by superb earthy poets. Both Sue and Bones were aware of my passionate love of music and poetry, they were relentless in their eager pursuit of stirring within me my lost desire to write.

'"I wandered lonely as a cloud/That floats on high o'er vales and hills,/When all at once I saw a crowd,/A host, of golden daffodils."'

The words flowed from Sue's sincere lips like falling summer rain, splashing over my melting heart.

When Sue's transparent blue eyes reddened with the strain of night reading, Bones would take his turn at the thick, leather-bound book. His choice of poems was all to do with lost love and man's secret yearning to love and be loved.

Without the restrictions of formality, it was evident to Sue that sleepy Bones and I were mentally in love with each other, for we innocently gave her the uneasy feeling that she was no more than an unwanted intruder. Bones and I were buzzing together on the same wavelength, we were wired up on to the same electric socket, stimulating one another by just being near to each other. I think clever Sue had suspected something about our unusual friendship for a long time, for where I trod Bones' loyal feet would follow like an affectionate, loving watch dog. If I was down, then so was he, and if I was high then Bones was happy too. The pair of us were so infectious it would be madness to think no one in Rachel would notice.

There was still a very important part of my senses missing, my sexual urges. It disturbed me greatly, for as much as I wanted to be with Bones I just couldn't fancy him making love to me in bed. In any case I couldn't really recognise love because I had never been friends with any man before.

What kind of crazy light must Bones and I have cast upon the atmosphere of Rachel? A blind, cockney, suicidal maniac walking hand in hand with a short-sighted, paranoid Japanese upon a cloud of fantasy and childish reality. Little wonder Dr Bright set about her plan of destroying the bizarre assocation of two of her star subjects.

I was woken by Sue at seven o'clock with my morning injection of insulin. I then staggered along the dim corridor towards the breakfast room. My half-closed eyes were stinging in their red-rimmed sockets, for it was only three hours earlier I had left Sister's smoky office and crawled wearily beneath the cool white sheets of the bed. I fully expected myself to be the only sleepy one present at the breakfast table, thinking Bones would not stir from his slumber until late morning, being as he spent most of the early morning in the unenviable task of reciting poems of my taste.

But to my surprise, there he was, in his usual seat, waiting in loyal readiness to serve me my daily portion of porridge. We politely bade each other good morning. Bones was so alert and active, it was made obvious that he had not slept, although he insisted he had slept so light, the faint sound of the food trolley had woken him.

I don't know what enticed me to say it, but my words popped from my lips as quick and sudden as a champagne cork.

'I love you, Bones,' said I, without lifting my gaze from my half-filled bowl of milky cereal.

Bones gave the habitual suck on his side-gum.

'No, I don't think you do, Rosie.'

'But I don't lie, Bones, except for when I want to get myself out of trouble.'

Bones smiled and unnecessarily stirred the small silver spoon resting in his tea cup.

'I'm not saying you are a liar, Rosie, it just seems to me you have never been in touch with a nice guy before, I mean one who doesn't beat up his wife and mess around bars, but I'm not really a nice guy myself.'

I pushed my empty bowl away and sipped at my waiting tea.

'I can't understand you, Bones, why do you dislike yourself so much?'

Bones pushed a cigarette into my mouth and nervously lit it.

'Honest, Rosie, there are hundreds of nice guys in this world, it's just unlucky you've not come across one yet. I just can't take advantage of your naive romantic nature. For the first time in my life, let me do something good. I don't want to use you like some chicken-shit broad, you are a woman of a rare fine quality, don't let any bum like me make you dirty.'

I felt stupid, childish and rejected. I simply had to cover up my pangs of hurt and embarrassment.

'But I can love you, Bones, without getting too involved, after all, I love Lucy, Frenchie and Empty, but it doesn't mean I want to jump into bed with them.'

Now we were the same inside for Bones' sad face twisted with hurt embarrassment.

I think maybe Bones' philosophy of my true make-up could have been correct, for never had I been tenderly kissed by any adult being, unless it was on the blunt pretext of receiving something in return. My mind was in such confusion about the fact that there were people in the world who were willing to give me a small piece of their precious time, people who cared and held out their soft hands to others who had got lost along the way. Funny that I after living on this earth for so long never really knew that kind of man existed, except in dreams.

'Hello, Mrs Logan,' smiled Mr Curtis, pumping my hand up and down with confident strength.

Energetic Mr Curtis was my blind-welfare officer, and had decided to pay me a visit in Rachel.

'Now, how are you keeping these days?'

I assured him that I was in good health and that Dr Bright was extremely pleased with my progress.

Mr Curtis had come to discuss my transfer to the blind rehabilitation centre at Torquay, Devon. He was a slight, short man in his late fifties, silver-haired and bespectacled. I thought at the time what a splendid travelling salesman he would make as he sat

vividly explaining all the wonderful oppor-
tunities waiting for me in the beautiful, hilly
pastureland of Devon. I listened with slug-
gish interest, not truly caring if I was going
or not. Mr Curtis was very particular with
his immaculate appearance, forever tidying
his white shirt-cuffs, straightening his blue-
spotted tie, and unnecessarily brushing the
knees of his blue serge trousers.

'Now, the main aim of this course is to
teach you some sort of a trade that will enable
you to play a useful role in society. Rosie,
you will be amazed at the confidence that
this course will give you, you'll come home
a new woman.'

After an hour of Mr Curtis's doing most
of the talking, I was informed by Sister that
it was time for the important daily group
talk. Mr Curtis gathered himself together,
making sure his appearance was its same
perfect self, then bade me farewell, after
which I joined the rest of the waiting circle.
I tripped between Empty and God and slid
inconspicuously into a soft orange chair.

*

We all sat silent for five or so minutes. Lucy was absent for she was in her room sleeping off her first dose of ECT.

'I wanna talk about my inferiority complex,' said a crude, cockney-voiced man in his mid-twenties. 'I work up the City in the stock exchange and I'm a dealer.' He pulled the thin wrapper off a stick of chewing gum and nervously popped it into his talking lips. 'My workmates are all toffee-nosed creeps who talk right la-de-da, and every bloody time I open my mouth they take the piss out of me just because I talk like a cockney.'

Dr Scramble asked if the self-conscious speaker was ashamed of his true environment.

The instant reply was, 'Yes, I am.'

One patient suggested that the man should go to evening classes in order to improve his vocabulary, another thought a change of employment may help. Someone even came up with the crazy idea of the man becoming a hit man for Mothercare. Their absurd suggestions were making my skin crawl with fury as they went on and on, round in circles, getting absolutely nowhere. Once again I found I had to say my piece.

'Do you know how the word cockney came about?' I asked, and I was astonished to find not one person did, my audience was extremely quiet and impressed as I carried on telling my story of what I thought was common knowledge to every East Londoner.

My tale began hundreds of years ago when London was made up of wealthy bank and ship merchants. London was the centre of golden coins and high finance, while only a few miles away toiling on the rich farmlands of England were the common field workers, grafting under the hard supervision of greedy landowners, for a mean weekly sum of pennies, barely enough to keep their hungry children from entering the cruel door of starvation. On these work farms, if a chicken laid a bad egg, the locals would call it a cocklay. At the same time there was springing up amongst the farming families a rare group of both men and women who would no longer tolerate the landowners' abuse of their back-breaking labour. So these few selected young people decided to revolt and make their impoverished ways to the capital of

England, considering themselves worthy of receiving a piece of the cake which they had helped to make. These humble revolutionaries hung around the edge of London, skiving and diving around until they multiplied and grew into self-made communities such as Bethnal Green, Aldgate, Hoxton and so on.

I ended my talk by addressing the cockney man with a pat of congratulation on his new proud back.

'We are the cream of society, mate, we come from true revolutionaries who had the spunk to stand up and fight for a piece of the cake.'

I guessed horrible Oliver would want to jump on the wagon and he did.

Oliver puffed on his extra-long cigarette and boastfully announced, 'Actually, it is believed my ancestors were of cockney origin, the salt of the earth, you know.'

While enviable Oliver and the cockney gent sat bickering over their true identity and place of birth, God stood in the centre of the floor bowing and worshipping the large plastic clock placed on the wall above the electric fire.

'Forgive them, Father, for they know not what they say.'

Frenchie sat in a far-off corner, trying to convince the uninterested group that the nasty French Algerians were planning to kidnap her in the night.

Well, thought I, smiling, at least they kept quiet while I did my thing.

So proud was I of my place of birth, the unique intelligence of my cherished father and the proud, hard-working dignity of my deprived mother, my heart would burst into a rage of fiery anger if anyone dared knock my ancestors.

I could remember seeing, before my eyes faded away, the faces of the East End women waiting at bus stops, shopping in the bustling market or dragging their limp bodies along the grey back streets towards home after toiling all day long in some sweaty factory. Each face wearing the same drawn, tired expression, yet the women never took time to complain or question their existence. How different the faces I passed by when walking through the West End. Women with ivory, wrinkle-free profiles and soft, fussed-over hair, and oh, how beautifully soft and well-cared for were their hands. Yet these soft, lovely women were those who fought and complained about equal rights for us down-trodden females. If I had one pound note for every married woman raped each night by her legal slave master, then I would surely be a millionairess. Until they started educating the men, then women's liberty would always be nothing more than a load of bullshit to those women trapped in the web of man's ignorance.

CHAPTER TWELVE

'Hello, Nuts, anything exciting happened in the madhouse today?'

Jim strolled into my room, it was New Year's Eve and Dr Bright had given me consent to spend two days at home. Jim had kept his promise by turning up at Rachel to escort me, for I was beginning to miss Mark and Sarah even if they did fight like cat and dog most of the time.

Jim stood rocking on his long thin legs, much the worse for drink.

'You ready then, Nutcase?'

I gave no reply, for past experience had taught me to be silent.

Nurse Liz came in looking sadly concerned for my safety, asking if I was sure I could cope. I sensed she did not look with approval at Jim's unsteady, spiteful-tongued behaviour. Being a rather good actress I left the ward as if I were overjoyed at the prospect of spending New Year with my family.

Jim was drunkenly rough in the handling of my person when we left the hospital, he allowed me to misjudge my steps and I fell – thud – down the hospital's stone stairs. On reaching Whitechapel tube station I was sweating with fear after stumbling helplessly down the short flight of busy stairs leading on to the bustling platform. The noisy rumbling train was packed tight with foreign voices, smoke and unfamiliar smells.

Jim and I stood nose to nose swaying in rhythm to the fast movement of the steaming tube. Jim's hot breath smelt heavy and sour as the close fumes of drink flowed over my sweating face.

My thoughts ran back to my last beating. My friends had tried to cheer me up by suggesting I join them in a night out on the town. But as much as they tried I could not enter into the spirit of happy conversation, because at the time I was dying inside slowly and painfully.

I arrived home at about two o'clock in the
morning and was just about to prepare myself
a cup of hot milk when bang, bang, bang
thundered on the street door, instantly I knew
it was drunken Jim. Mark woke with fright at
the mad frenzied banging, he leapt down the
stairs with worried haste.

'Mum, it's Daddy, where can I hide you?'

My heart was bursting from my breast.
Where do I run, how can I run? I can't see
where I'm running to.

Suddenly the back garden door was echoing with Jim's angry fists. Mark immediately
had a good brainwave.

'Mum,' whispered Mark, leading me up the
dark hallway towards the front door, 'you run
as fast as you can, you can hide up Aunt
Lil's, and I'll take my time in letting Daddy
in through the back way.'

Mark pushed me out of the door into darkness, but where was I running and how could
I find Aunt Lil's flat? Everything was black, I
wasn't capable of finding my own feet. Bang,
something hit me full in the chest and I fell
flat on my back with a sickening thud. I
had fled smack into a darkened car. I sat

in the damp gutter not knowing what had so viciously attacked my fleeing body.

'Oh, someone help me, it's so terribly dark, please, someone, lead me away, I just can't take any more.'

I screamed in agony for my hair was being ripped from my aching scalp. It was Jim, he was upon me like an insane beast of the unknown, he was dragging me by the hair and flicking his hard foot – crack – into the bottom of my spine. Then I was sagging in the armchair in the living-room.

I couldn't feel anything as Jim rained blow after blow each side of my numbed head. I didn't cry or speak as if I were hoping for the final punch that would conveniently end my miserable life.

Mark screamed, 'Dad, what's the matter with you, how can you beat a blind woman?'

Mark rushed between Jim and me, standing upright in front of me. He was tall and strong, staring at his father.

'You're not going to beat Mummy any more, Dad.'

Mark never stirred, he stood in calm defiance as Jim roared at his small tender face,

'Move, you little cunt, or so help me I'll break your fucking back.'

Mark sat on my dead lap and stretched his thin arms open wide, hoping to protect me.

'You'll have to kill me first, Dad, before I let you put a finger on Mummy, I love her, and I'm not going to stand back and let you hurt her any more.'

I am going to faint on this bloody train.

Sweat was running down my back and breasts, even my hair was damp with the perspiration clinging to the back of my neck.

I am going to die.

Jim dragged me from the standing train on to the platform of East Ham. I felt like a rag doll, for I had no bones in my limp useless body, no spine to keep me upright and my legs were paralysed.

'Please, Jim, I can't walk.' I begged him to sit me down for a while. As the sharp, cold December wind rushed along the open platform the sweat on my body turned icy cold. 'I think I am going to die.'

Jim sneered in disgust at my feebleness.

'You're one big fucking nuisance, you've

got to make a big thing over a poxy train ride now.'

After a cup of hot tea in a nearby café, I had regained a little of my lost confidence. Our next stage of the journey was to get on a 101 bus that would drop us off at my mother's council house at Wanstead. After alighting gracefully from the bus again I stumbled forward, scraping my shin on the high concrete kerb. By the time I reached my mother's home I was a complete mental and physical wreck.

'Good God,' shouted my mother, 'how come the doctor's let you come home in that state?'

After a nip of warm brandy, a cup of tea and a cigarette, I was half-way back to myself.

Mother visited me each Wednesday while I was in Rachel so she became quite friendly with my hospital friends. Mum was pleased to know Lucy was getting better, but sad to hear that Frenchie was soon to be transferred to an asylum. Jim interrupted the conversation with a sickly comment that made my blood run cold.

'Didn't you know, Rosie's being transferred

with Frenchie, Mad Maggie is what Dr Bright calls Rosie.'

I knew Dr Bright had been talking confidentially with Jim in her office each week.

So that's their crafty game, they want to lock me away in some weird madhouse full of cranks and nuts. But how could he? Jim promised me in the beginning he wouldn't sign my life away. Perhaps it's because my eyes are starting to wander, maybe it makes me look crazy when I stumble around like a big fool. But I'm not crazy, my mind is bright and active, I talk sense and I can hear and understand what people are saying.

In the darkness of the taxi home I never spoke a single word, in fear I might say something that would condemn me as a lunatic.

I tried to eat my late meal but I couldn't, for my windpipe was blocked and the food just wouldn't pass down my throat. In any case, the tedious process of swallowing took far too much of my energy.

Jim thumped the table and snapped at me.

'If you don't eat that dinner, I'll ram it down your fucking neck.'

I snapped, for I remember bursting into tears, and pushing my full plate to one side. I ran to my bed and stayed there until the following morning.

I started the day by filling a small china basin with boiling water for the purpose of sterilising my glass syringe for my daily injection. How it truly happened I am not quite sure, but by accident I carelessly bumped into Jim, spilling the hot water all over his large hairy forearm. Jim screamed half with pain and half with temper. He slapped me full-pelt across the kitchen as if I were no more than a fragile cardboard figure, smashing my protruding hip bone against the sharp corner of the electric cooker. I immediately ran to the upstairs safety of my peaceful bedroom, leaving behind in my hasty retreat a trail of untidiness caused by my clumsy tripping feet.

I sat asking myself where can I go for help, for my survival was dependent upon my daily supply of insulin and tablets. But there was no way in which I could rely on myself, for I knew not how to draw up the required amount of insulin into my syringe, for my eyesight was far too weak to attempt such an important task. I thought of my mother, knowing full well she would help, even though her days were taken up with the unhappy task of caring for my sick stepfather.

'Mum, is that you?' I sobbed into the phone. 'Please, can you come over, it's twelve o'clock and I haven't had my pills or injection yet, and I think I am going mad.'

As I sobbed, I could hear Jim and the children in the closed living-room, they were laughing their heads off at some amusing television show. Jim pricked up his ears to my telephone conversation in the hall, and before my mother's speedy arrival Jim had hastily performed my injection.

When mother appeared she was not her usual aggressive self, I think it was the sight of my dirty, unkempt, helpless appearance that left her so surprisingly speechless. She tenderly wiped my swollen eyes with a rough, cool face cloth, gave me a cup of welcome tea. Mum left after first making sure I had eaten a cheese sandwich.

It was New Year's Day, the beginning of another dreaded year. I sat on the brown mock-velvet settee for the rest of the long endless day and no one spoke. Mark and Sarah seemed hostile towards my dead vacant expression. What an unnatural situation I was in, surrounded by so-called loved ones and yet my inner self dying slowly with loneliness. I had to weep, holding my heavy head in my limp hands, I rocked and wept like a rejected infant until Jim snapped into one of his pop-eyed brainstorms.

'I am sick of you and your poxy crying, I put up with you all over Christmas sitting like a fucking imbecile.' He jumped to his feet, clenching his plastic teeth and frothing angry white foam from his cruel distorted mouth. 'You're nothing but a fucking old shit cunt and we don't want you here, a blind useless whore – fuck off back to the nut house where you belong!'

I screamed long and loud, shaking my head in mad frenzy.

'I don't want to live, somebody help me to die.'

With a crazy burst of energy I leapt to my feet and began groping around the living-room, knocking things over in mad tormented frustration. 'I can't live with this darkness, I want to see, or fucking die.'

Jim took hold of my trembling wrist with such force I felt his sharp, relentless nails bite savagely into my thin fleshless wrists.

I remember no more of the three days I spent playing with the strange patterns of blood dancing about behind my sight. On the third night, Jim, dressed in his best attire, went to a public house, and didn't return that evening, leaving poor tormented Mark responsbile for my complete well-being. Behind my growing thoughts of death and release, I was still sane enough to realise my unhappy son just could not cope with my constant attempts at suicide. For I had deliberately filled the syringe with insulin and four times injected my belly hoping to send myself off into a fatal coma. Finding this unsuccessful, I swallowed the remainder of my antidepressant pills, to discover the only effect on my person was the husky loss of my voice.

I simply had to relieve Mark and Sarah of their burden, so I impulsively telephoned for a taxi to take me back to Rachel. The driver led me to his waiting car. I had not washed

or combed my tangled hair or eaten for three
nightmare days. How my presence must have
disturbed the unknowing taxi man as I sat
next to him on our journey to the London
Hospital. He sat, nervous and silent, trying
desperately to take his curious gaze away
from my vacant-eyed person. I was still in my
nightdress and slippers which smelt sickly,
heavy with stale sweat, caused by countless
hypo events.

When I reached Rachel, Sister Jackie
greeted my demented state with her sympathy
and sincere concern. I sat on my bed, looking
mistily up into Jackie's kind face.

'Please, Jackie, where is your sense of
compassion? Why make me live if I don't
want to?'

The tears fell down my cheeks like a constant hot spring. Jackie swallowed a huge
lump that had built up in her dry throat.

'I know how you feel, Rosie, but we are
here to save life, not to destroy it, no matter
how much the person suffers.' Jackie passed
me a soft paper tissue on which I wiped my
running salty nose.

'But Jackie, I'm not crazy, it's people who

put me here and I have no control over their cruel doings — please don't make me live through all these awful events.'

'Now come on, Rosie, take your clothes off,' demanded a stern Jamaican nurse, standing with her small hands resting on her hipless body. She had led me to the green-tiled bathroom, filled the bath with hot water and was now waiting for my grubby body to plunge into the waiting disinfectant. She spoke to me as if I were a naughty little girl who had thoughtlessly run through a field of muddy grass. She brought back a feeling inside of me that I had long forgotten.

I was nine or ten at the time. I stood with a host of skeleton children and we were all completely naked, boys and girls alike. We were in the local cleansing station waiting and shivering with the autumn cold. Some had scabies and some were the victims of lice and fleas. A huge-breasted, white-overalled woman held a rough, hairy distemper brush in her big hand which she kept on dipping into a large bowl filled with a pink smelly creamy mixture.

'Open your legs,' said she coldly, and I obeyed.

She was painting me all over with the pink stinging mixture. Like sheep, we frightened children were then plunged into a steaming hot bath of strong-smelling water, just like on the great sheep farms of Australia.

The nurse disturbed my thoughts by telling me, 'Rosie you must never neglect your personal appearance again. How could you neglect your lovely hair, just look at it, looks like you haven't combed it for a week.'

After bathing and then showering my body with sweet-smelling talcum powder, I must admit I felt better than I had done in a long time.

CHAPTER THIRTEEN

It was made bitterly obvious my past undisciplined behaviour at home would not be
tolerated by Jim, for in the weeks to follow
the absence of my immediate family gave me
the hard facts of the matter. I had unwill-
ingly joined the ranks of the abandoned,
the unwanted, who were much the greater
part of Rachel's occupants. I was penniless,
the same as Frenchie, without any source
of income. I had to teach myself the fine
art of poncing. My pride and vanity made
it hurtfully difficult for me to accept the
sickening truth that I was a bum or beggar,
whichever label suited me. My only contact
now with the outside world was with that of
my generous mother and my devoted friend

Jenny, who sometimes stuffed a crisp pound note into my well-worn jeans pocket.

As they left the ward on each occasion I closed the door of my room, pulled down the flowered blind over the see-through window and cried, for I was aching inside for the beautiful sound of Mark and Sarah's spring-like voices. I longed for the touch of Sarah's tiny pink hands and the feel of Mark's brown silky crown, remembering how I always ruffled the top of his clever head saying, 'All right, son.' Why oh why were Jim and the children so ashamed of my being placed in a psychiatric unit? Why did they try so hard to hide the unpleasant fact from their mocking friends? For I was not mentally deficient because I tended to break things, burn the dinner and fall about.

Dr Bright tried to comfort my loneliness by explaining the strange ways of a child's mind. It seemed that when something frightening threatened a child's bright future, he tended to pretend it was not really there, hoping it would eventually disappear. The main cause of my mental breakdown was that Mark and Sarah would simply not believe I was going blind.

But how long will it take to educate my bewildered family, or will it take for ever?

As I lay on my bed I could hear Oliver being exceedingly helpful to rambling Lucy. Oliver was insisting that Lucy take his full pack of fresh cigarettes. Oliver had changed as if by magic, from a rude selfish bigot into a kind, considerate, gentle man. It suddenly dawned on me why I was once so distressed over his sick personality. Oliver was Jim and if Jim was the same as past Oliver then Jim was a schizophrenic and in need of help.

'Doing a bit of thinking, Rosie?' smiled Dr Bright, sliding slowly towards my usual place of meditation, which was my well-worn bed.

'Ain't much else I can do, is there?' I sighed.

Dr Bright did not pursue my sullen remark of boredom, she rested elegantly down into the small, leather easy chair, crossing her high, black suede boots with ladylike precision.

'I would like to ask you if you would mind being the subject for the professor's lecture. All you will be expected to do is answer a few questions which the professor may ask you.' Dr Bright looked hopeful of my consent. 'You

can refuse if you wish, Rosie, but I would be
very happy if you would allow us to use you
as our subject.'

'My, what an honour,' grinned Bones an
hour later after I had told him of my instant
agreement to displaying my mind's eye in
full view of a gathering of top-daddy psychia-
trists. 'You must be a pretty bright woman,
Rosie, for Dr Bright to choose you as her star
patient.'

No one had ever thought me clever before,
and I didn't know how to answer.

'Want a tangerine, Bones?' smiled I, throwing the orange fruit on to his blue-denim
lap.

Bones peeled his tangerine with the fine
skill of a brain surgeon, and as always he held
the upside-down skin in his steady palm.

'There, perfect,' boasted he. 'Looks like
the skin has not been broken.'

I complimented happy Bones on his splendid achievement.

'I know you're screwed up, Rosie,' said he,
jumping back to the subject. 'You were born
in the wrong place, at the wrong time, and
what can any head doctor do about that?'

My hand trembled as I pushed a section of tangerine into my thirsty mouth.

'Oh, don't tell me that, Bones. You're saying there's no chance of me ever getting better.'

Bones' piercing, slant eyes travelled searchingly over my whole person, starting from my fluffy house-slippers, over my knees to my small pot belly, up to my well-proportioned breasts and ending at the fixed gaze set in my foggy eyes.

'If you're crazy, Rosie, then I'll keep praying you'll never get better.'

'Hi, Stumbles,' interrupted Lucy, bursting into my room. 'I've just seen the television people, they are coming to do *This Is Your Life*.'

Lucy dived at my polished wardrobe, opened its squeaking door and began fiddling around my personal belongings. I never made any attempt to stop her bizarre actions for I knew she felt happy, and who was I to interfere with such a secret joy?

Bubbling Lucy was the make-up artist, the hairdresser, director, producer, and camera team, all working together in perfect blissful harmony, making my drab appearance beautiful enough to be the shining star of a famous television programme.

Lucy stood back, glowing with a sense of brilliant creation.

'Oh, Stumbles, you look so beautiful, everyone in the world will fall in love with you.'

I knew I resembled an overdone clown, with my face covered in snow-white talcum powder, my lips over-enlarged with bright-red lipstick and my long black hair pinned scraggily on top of my head like an abandoned crow's nest. So hypnotic was Lucy's enthusiasm, even watching Bones had to admit how ravishing lovely I looked. Why, time after time, I fell like a blind fool into Lucy's traps of mad fantasy, I'll never know. But each time she decided to go on a trip into the world of sweet unreality, I felt as though I wanted to go with her. In times of sadness and tears I even had the crazy notion to join Lucy's world of joy for ever and ever, but in truth I gladly returned after each wonderful trip.

The new day came in a burst of unexpected cold, for the month was January, the time of year when flowers hide in waiting patience for the warm sun, and mighty trees stand rigid in natural protection against the merciless winds, and people smother their cold bodies with thick woollen winter garments of sure security against the foggy morning frost.

Sunbeams broke into the dull day room and gently waded along the wooden-lined corridors of Rachel, unnoticed by the busy affray of patients. One long lingering sunbeam rested upon my cheek, warming my right eyelid, making it open and close in response to the brightness.

'Tell me, Mrs Logan, how did you feel when you were first told you were a diabetic?' said the aged professor, peering over the top of his gold wire spectacles.

I turned to his voice. 'OK, I suppose. The doctor told me they might come up with a cure some day, but some day never came.'

I was seated on a hard wooden chair placed on a six-inch-high platform running along one end of the classroom. Beside me was a wide desk with chairs all around, and seated in these neatly arranged stools of comfort with pale faces as serious as death there was Dr Bright, Dr Pretty, and two wise-looking professors.

The mass of people sitting silent and still in front of me was made up of Long Dog, Margaret my social worker, Dr Dee from the diabetic unit, and a large amount of young, eager students of psychology. The kindly professor continued his gentle interrogation of me.

'You have had a book of your poems published, haven't you, Mrs Logan?'

I nodded in acknowledgement, yes.

'And does your family show interest in your work?'

I shrugged my shoulders and replied, 'Not really, I just write for myself, anyway the publisher cut me up and my book can't be put on sale now.'

The wise-looking man at the far end of the table spoke with warmth and understanding as he asked, 'Tell me, Rosie, would you like to continue writing?'

'I can't,' said I, swallowing with great difficulty, 'not now, I'm nearly blind.'

'And why not, Rosie?'

My bottom lip was starting to tremble as it always did when I was on the verge of tears.

I must not cry and belittle myself, it's all right saying keep a stiff upper lip, but what about my bottom one? Oh balls, why not come out with the shameful truth, I'm half illiterate, I can't spell and I only know about a dozen proper words apart from swear words, that is.

'You see, doctor, I can't write without a dictionary.' I began to stutter in trying to communicate with such a learned gathering. 'It's words like search I can't write, I searched and when I searched I found after searching, it just don't sound right, does it? So I go to a dictionary and I find different words that mean the same thing, I mean there's seek, pursue, oh and lots more, I find words that I never knew existed. So how do I write without eyes to find what I am looking for? I just don't know enough words to write in darkness.'

After much debate my learned audience came up with one major solution which was to get me as quick as possible on to the rehabilitation course for the newly blind.

*

How I dreaded the let-down when Rachel became swamped with noisy marching visitors, the distant echoes of their talking laughter ringing in my empty lonely ears. In the blackness of the street outside, a long stream of rainbow-coloured cars ran to and fro, like a huge trail of disciplined glow-worms, each one in front determined to reach its destination before any of the twin lights following behind.

I listened to the buzzing, honking vehicles below my window and dreamed, longing for the back seat of one white glowing chariot on the bustling road to be occupied by smiling Mark and Sarah, their hearts bursting with joy at the thought of travelling to visit their waiting mother. But my dream was so very long in coming true.

If only I could see, I would run from Rachel and leap on to a train just as fast as my aching heart could take me, for I was homesick and crying inside for the long-lost sound of my two children's voices.

If it had not been for Jenny I am almost certain I would have crumbled away, just like Frenchie. For while I sat marooned inside the walls of crazy Rachel, Jenny was making herself extremely busy informing all my lost, past friends of my unhappy defeated frame of mind. Jenny became a walking information bureau, explaining my distress to every one of my so-called friends, and her exhausting efforts blossomed into a beautiful flow of kind, loving visitors, laden with gifts.

My sincere guests came in unexpected forms, for they were the friends I never truly thought would comfort me when in need. Yet the ones who I had expected to care, my real close friends and family, found it impossible to find enough time to give me the pleasure of their company. How funny the ways of teaching a person who their true friends really were.

During my stay in Rachel I had been more educated about the strange ways of society than I had ever learned in my previous thirty or more years. The old saying was live and learn, but I thought the extreme reverse: die and learn.

I think when I die I will be scientifically cremated, and my flaky ashes scattered to the four waiting winds, and one day with a little bit of luck Mark and Sarah will walk along a crowded street and perhaps a tiny fragment of my dust will fall upon their cheeks and I shall touch and caress them without anyone else in the world being made aware of such lovely contact. I also think that, being as I have endlessly longed to see another piece of the great earth, apart from London, from which I have never strayed, maybe the strong breath of fate will blow a piece of my lingering ashes on to a fast sailing ship that will eventually carry me on to some beautiful sun-kissed island full of free-growing sweet tangerines, and there I shall sit in the shape of a soft cornflake. Looking out across the blue and green peaceful ocean, yes, I say to myself, I must most certainly be cremated. But then I think with my bad luck I would most likely end up on the bony, starving dog, begging outside the wealthy door of some Chinese brothel. But not to dwell on such matters until the hand of time beckons me to do so.

Someone switched on the electric light. I sat, rubbing my eyes against the sudden brightness.

'Rosie, it's me, Jenny.'

I stood and greeted her by throwing my arms

around her narrow shoulders and squeezing her tightly, for I was hungry for company and human bodily contact.

'What you sitting in the dark for?' snapped Jenny, as she placed two large packs of my favourite cigarettes on the cluttered top of my bedside cabinet.

'I'm fucking sick of this place,' groaned I in self-pity.

'There's plenty who are worse off than you,' insisted snappy Jenny, filling my empty plastic fruit bowl with fresh-bought fruit. 'You are coming to the pub with me tomorrow night, sitting here in the bloody dark, what on earth's the matter with you? It's about time you started getting out and about.'

Jenny had just had her strawberry-red hair fixed into a short, roaring-twenties style, and how well it blended with her large, watery, grey-green eyes. How I envied her love of living.

'I can't go out, Jenny.' I dropped my blood-stained eyes down on to my tatty flowered blouse and badly stained, faded denims. 'All I've got to wear is what I'm sitting in, except for a pair of dirty trousers there in the wardrobe.'

Jenny swiftly opened my empty cupboard, retrieving my modern pair of lime-green pants. She stood, examining their messy state, saying, 'Now then, Rosie, I'll take these home with me tonight, won't take me long to wash and press them, I'll bring them back tomorrow night so you just be ready and waiting. You can wear them when I take you to our pub.'

I tried to think of some good excuse to prevent me going out.

'I don't think I can drink, Jenny.'

'And why not?'

'The drugs I'm on, I don't think they mix too well with drink.'

'All right,' barked Jenny with impatience, 'so you can sit at the bar and drink coffee. You can chat with the other customers, at least it will be a change of scenery, this place would bore anyone to tears. Rosie, you've got to help yourself because no other bastard will.' Jenny stopped talking and snapped her thin finger and thumb in remembrance of something very important. 'Oh Rosie, I almost forgot to tell you, Ray the Sus came over our pub with Tommy Tippy-toes. When I told them you have been here for the past six weeks, they really done their nuts to think no one had told them before.' Jenny's cheeks glowed with flushed excitement. 'And guess what, Rosie, Joe Piano has finished the first song for your musical and its a fantastic knockout. Ray the Sus said you are going to be a rich woman.'

I burst into tears of joy.

'Oh Jenny, I can't believe it, you mean they truly like my book?'

'Like it?' beamed Jenny, 'they fucking love it, you're going to make such bread you just won't know how to spend it.'

After Jenny left, I sat spellbound by her story of my success. Ordinary me, a common old East Ender, blind, penniless, uneducated me, fancy I wrote a book that's going to be made into a marvellous musical. I didn't believe they were impressed with my funny old manuscript of *A Necessary Evil*. I only wrote it because I wanted to say something, and when two top professional writers like Ray the Sus and Tippy-toes said they wanted to write it into a musical script, I thought they were just being polite. Even when the producer introduced me to Joe Piano, who

was such a famous and successful composer,
I still couldn't really believe it.

It was like a big beautiful dream. I tugged
at my hair and winced, just to make positively
sure I was real.

CHAPTER FOURTEEN

My days were growing shorter, and my long nights less empty, for everything was going smooth for me. I was being visited three or more times a week. Margaret my social worker was busy with the blind-welfare people who were supplying me with a Braille dictionary and many other books. My spirit was high and I was looking forward to the day when I would be able to read with my fingertips.

Tippy-toes' wife Peggy was visiting me every Friday with a collection of the most sensible gifts like diabetic jam, so that I could enjoy real jam on my small bread ration at tea time. She also caringly brought me a large jar of granulated coffee, in fact, everything a hospital patient needed, even two pairs of clean knickers and a dozen sanitary towels.

So personal were Peg's gifts I knew she must have had a heart as big as a pumpkin.

It wasn't pills that were making me better, it was people. I began to think myself not so unlucky after all. My most exciting day was when Tippy-toes bounced into my room with his spring-heeled steps, he was full of gaiety and alertness as he bubbled on about my musical. Tippy-toes was a man of immense natural rhythm. Even his brisk way of walking showed his self-taught talent of dancing as light and airy as a soft rhythmic balloon. What a shame Tippy-toes' talent was held down with the tight-spring trap of money.

We went to the kitchen to make a pot of tea, and Ray the Sus must have smelt its fine brew, for he arrived just as Tippy-toes was pouring. Ray the Sus was grinning, his sensitive eyes the exact shade of a crisp five-pound note. Ray was an ex-school teacher with a busy-body mind, suspecting all who came before him. He looked at you like he was a headmaster and you were one of his crafty young pupils. Joe Piano was late, as usual. Even after purchasing a fast motor bike, Joe was still always late for any arranged appointment. He was six foot and slender, in his early thirties and prematurely bald, his lean shoulders drooping down with the tremendous weight of his own brilliance.

'Are we all sitting comfortable?' smiled Ray the Sus. 'Then I shall begin.'

He placed Joe Piano's tape recording into my cheap-sounding cassette player. The song was of one of my characters named Jimmy Jesus. So deliriously wonderful was Joe Piano's production of the sound of the beautiful, heart-tearing violins, it filled me with something that happened fifteen years earlier, when I first gave birth to a tiny, pink human being, the marvellous inner sense of creation, a lost feeling I thought I would never experience again.

After the music ended, my three buzzing life-savers sat and zestfully ran through the entire script, which at this stage was only a rough synopsis of my book. My mind dazzled with delight, for I had as my partners three of the cream in the writing game, each one perfect in their selected roles: Joe Piano excellent in the field of music, and Tippy-toes, an ex-jail bird, was superb for the authenticity of East End verbal, and clever

Ray, portly Ray the Sus, was our conductor, the man who kept us all in line, and who was also highly educated in complicated words of great importance.

How everything was happening in my favour. Even Lucy was made to progress after being jerked with the last of her six ECT treatments. Although I selfishly missed her lost personality, for now at the morning group sessions Lucy sat sullen, quiet and depressed. And I heard that God was next in line for electro-convulsive therapy. But Bones was getting worse, for he was deliberately breaking off communication with other people and sulking on the dull monotony of his bed, where he lay listlessly looking up at the tall white ceiling. We each in turn tried to coax him out of his doldrums. But Bones was stubborn and indifferent to our concerned manner. He had taken himself to another world, and no way were we able to entice Bones back to the reality of Rachel.

Bones was much happier when Lucy and I were at our worst, for since our vast improvement he seemed extraordinarily discontent with our change. Once scatterbrained Lucy was now quiet, sensible and ladylike, while I who was so very silent and remorseful was now burning with an ever-growing inner confidence. No more did I creep around Rachel with slow, humble steps, my head was now upright and full of hope.

'Hello, Bones,' said I, as he crept sorrowfully into my room.

It had been three or four days since he had paid me a visit, which was very unusual indeed for Bones had previously spent more of his time in my room than he did in his own sleeping compartment.

Bones sank into the chair, sighing with deep depression, 'I am going home, Rosie.'

His sad statement shocked me.

'When?' I asked quickly.

He first gave me a cigarette before answering my question.

'Dr Bright said I should fly back to California as soon as possible.'

My heart sank heavy and fast for I would miss him so terribly, especially for our late nights spent chatting, and drinking endless pots of tea. I wanted to fall on my knees and beg him not to go for Bones was the only person I had ever had the luck of meeting who truly understood me inside out. But no one empties their heart out telling all their inner thoughts, not unless they are some kind of crank.

I changed the subject by asking Bones if he had started writing yet, because two weeks earlier he had mentioned that he was thinking of starting a diary, about the day-by-day interesting events in Rachel. Bones lifted his sagging head and half-smiled at me.

'No, Rosie, I only mentioned it hoping the thought might encourage you to start writing again.'

I sat fiddling with the large tiger-eye ring on my third finger, trying to think up a sensible reply.

'I am afraid there's no chance of my ever writing again, Bones, I wouldn't know how to go about it now, although *Rosie in Rachel* would make a good title for a book.'

Bones grinned with instant joy as though he had just done some wonderful good deed.

'That's real bright of you, Rosie, it would sure make a swell title.'

Suddenly a loud, piercing scream broke

our creative concentration, and a red, cork-heeled, chunky sandal whizzed past my door hitting the opposite wall with a heavy thud.

'It's a ghost, it's a ghost,' called the distant voice.

Bones stared at the fallen sandal and laughed.

'Have you met the new patient yet, Rosie? She's next door to you and boy, is she crazy. Her mother sure must have a sense of humour, guess what the screaming shoe-thrower's name is – Nora Bone.' He smacked his knee with delight. 'Now, ain't that something to write about, Nora Bone.'

Bones kept repeating the name and shaking his smiling face. I witnessed Bones' change of personality and I thought how instant and easy his self-control was, he went from grief to comedy in one split-second. Bones could fly high and free as a gay kite and crash back down to earth as soon as the wind-change commanded him to do so.

'You're a right chameleon, ain't you, Bones?' laughed I, poking his tight shoulder. 'Quick as a flash, you can turn on and off whenever you want.'

Three days later Bones was saying his sad farewell to each patient. His two expensive travelling cases were packed full and waiting inside Rachel's entrance. He stroked my long soft hair with sensitive affection.

'Bye, Rosie, and don't let this get you down too much.'

Oh balls to convention, the stiff upper lip and all that cobblers. All I knew is that I felt sexy and I wanted to hold him in my empty aching arms.

As Bones turned his back to walk away I called out his name and rushed towards him. We stood holding each other for a full brief minute, rocking together like a pair of lost, hungry infants.

I dreamed of all the things I wanted to say: Bones, please take me with you to where the sun always shines, take me to a beach full of sugar sand and ice-cream cornets, and I will write the finest book of love poems that the world has ever read. But I spoke not a word for this was the story of my life, always wanting something I couldn't have.

Bones is gone taking a part of me back

to America with him. I must try to stop giving parts of me away to others for if I don't I will end up with nothing left to give. My father took the biggest chunk and since then I have been emptying out slowly year by year. I must not get so involved with people or I shall become hollow like the fruitless tangerine skins that Bones used to make.

Many of the group's participants were showing signs of sentimentality over Bones' departure. God sat thoughtfully looking at Nora as if trying to analyse her weird ways.

Nora was a slim black girl of eighteen. Her short, fuzzy hair was plaited into a maze of tiny twists, her eyes were big and lost, and Nora's thick lips were dripping with spit. She wore a little short, girlish dress full of blue forget-me-nots and lace.

'Hallelujah, Hallelujah,' she yelled repeatedly.

God called across the room.

'I know what's wrong with Nora, she is possessed by the devil.'

Nora gave a wild scream of strong disapproval then leapt to her feet like a frightened wild cat. Nora pounded on God's head with her blue plastic handbag. God covered his battered head with his trembling hands and lifted his bony knees high in defence against Nora's forward body. God's dressing-gown fell open to reveal all he had been sparingly blessed with underneath. Nora suddenly stopped dead, turned and strolled back to her seat as though nothing had happened.

She looked straight at astonished Dr Scramble and calmly explained, 'I never beat him up, it was the devil.'

God had given Nora a licence to behave as she wished and Nora had taken full advantage of God's gift. I sussed silly Nora out as being quite a shrewd cookie. My suspicion was confirmed later in the day when I stumbled into pop-eyed Nora on my way to the toilet.

'Fuck off, white woman!' shouted angry Nora, pushing me roughly away from her person.

I stepped forward and glared at her.

'Don't call me white.' Nora jumped back as I continued shouting back at her. 'Only the dying and the dead are white and I am not either, I am coloured.'

Nora hissed at me mockingly then ran her fingers in circles on the side of her veined temple.

'You are crazy woman, I am coloured, you are white.'

I pursued our argument with as much noise as Nora.

'I am not white, I am pink, beige and red and I have as much colour as you, so don't call me white woman 'cause I don't like it.'

Nora raised her long slender arm ready to strike me, then, much to my surprise, she lowered her tone into a gentle whisper.

'I am sorry,' were Nora's last soft words and off she swayed singing, 'Hallelujah.'

After proving to Nora Bone that anyone could have a chip on their shoulder no matter what shade of skin they were born with, we soon became the best of friends. Although we quarrelled most of the time she never called me white woman again, instead Nora referred to me as a pink-faced nut. I found out why Nora had taken an instant dislike to God, for the day she came into the ward her

first shocking sight was of God walking along
the corridor stark naked. And he being slight
of build in every respect, this was not a very
pretty sight to behold. And Nora told him so
in the group meeting one comical morning.

'I think God is a bad bad man,' said she
in complete disgust, 'for when I have been
found streaking at least I had the decency to
keep my frilly knickers on.'

Nora had publicly scolded God after he had
offered me a cigarette, which I thought very
kind of him until he shattered my illusion of
his warm generosity by saying he liked giving
me cigarettes. This was because he thought,
to his joy, that when I placed one eagerly into
my mouth the cigarette represented a penis.

But after God's first couple of jerks of
electro-convulsive therapy he was growing
more and more boring – as dull as my next-
door neighbour back home.

Bones had gone and Lucy was going home
each day to her parents and God had stopped
streaking. Rachel was becoming dead to me,
for each patient was growing dim and lifeless. So monotonous was its atmosphere of

tablet-time and meals, I imagined that one morning I would be discovered dead in my room and that Dr Bright and Dr Scramble would come to my rigid corpse to analyse the sudden cause of my death.

In my mind's eye I saw Dr Scramble looking very distressed as he turned to puzzled Dr Bright saying, 'This poor woman has most definitely been bored to death,' and lifting my limp lifeless hand only to prove how it flopped back dead on the bed. 'Look, Dr Bright, see, Rosie has been bored stiff as a poker.'

'Dreaming again, Rosie?' said a soft man's voice from reality.

It was Empty standing at my open door, I beckoned him to enter.

'I am bored to tears, Empty, it's not one of my good days today. I feel so low I could scream.'

Empty, with his sweet calm manner of politeness, was placing a tray on to my side locker.

'What you want, my girl, is a nice cup of tea,' smiled he, pouring out a cup of steaming tea and placing it into my waiting hand.

Empty then took a small bright bottle from

his cardigan pocket, unscrewed its miniature cap and slid a little into my cup saying, 'There, a nice drop of brandy.' Empty pushed the hot liquid to my mouth. 'Go on, Rosie, it will do you the world of good.'

He lived in a poky, one-bedroom flat in Whitechapel, in a jungle of concrete and tall-shadowed dwellings. Empty's old age seemed bleak, fruitless and lonely, although Empty was not short of material things, for he owned an expensive modern car, and his bank book was not to be laughed at. He had worked very hard building up his own insurance agency, also he was not lacking in attractive lady friends. But none of his many lovers could come up to his standard of what a wife should be. Which was someone who had understanding, warmth, and love of simple pleasures.

'Fancy coming out for a drive?' said Empty sipping morishly at his brandy tea. 'I can pop home and get my car, and we could have a nice slow drive up to High Beech.'

High Beech was in the green heart of Epping Forest. Empty and I stood high on a hill overlooking the green mass of colour below. It was windy, and bitterly cold, we stood shivering, both trying to convince each other that we weren't really cold. Standing near by was a mobile café, a huge van with a flap-open side where within a fat jolly man clad in a fresh white industrial coat served shivering customers with cardboard beakers of hot tea, warm savoury pasties, and biscuits.

Empty gallantly dusted an old fallen log before seating me down. A few minutes later he returned with two beakers of tea. I assured him there was no need to purchase any food as I was not the least bit hungry. I felt as though kind Empty, who was twenty years my senior, was trying to woo me into an intimate relationship.

'There's a robin at your feet,' nudged Empty. 'Can you see him, Rosie?'

I wished he had not mentioned the fluffy robin redbreast who was pecking at pieces of scattered bread only two feet away. For I began to ache for the beautiful sight of the gay-winged creature, so near to me yet so far away. I could hear the clop of horses' hooves and children laughing, blackbirds singing and tiny sparrows chirping all round my sightless presence. Now I wanted to cry with self-pity, longing to see the wonder of spring.

Empty was fully aware of my sadness. He broke my solitude by taking my empty cup and throwing it into a nearby wire waste bin. Then he gently took my hand and pulled me to my feet.

'There's a mackerel sky up there, Rosie, I think it's going to rain.'

Empty continued his detailed description of the singing countryside as he led me over bumpy turfs of damp grass towards his stationary car.

'We will sit in the car and have a smoke before heading back,' said he, fussing over my every move as though I were a helpless child.

In the warm, snug enclosure of the smoke-filled car, Empty began to tell me about his secret inner self. His compulsive talking was mostly of his dead wife and his heavy dark fear of loneliness. I was of little comfort, because I was preoccupied with the thought of not getting involved with men. Involvement meant pain.

'Let's go back, Empty, I'm cold.'

Empty obeyed my blunt command with the sad obedience of a rejected lover.

Each day after our visit to High Beech Empty took enormous pains to provide me with constant afternoon outings of outstanding variety.

All my life I had been so accustomed to fighting for what I wanted. I found Empty's willingness to obey my slightest whim much too easy a game for my cunning self-taught condition. I only wanted what I couldn't have and this was my upbringing, the fighting spirit that made me tick. My home, my children, everything that I possessed had been mine because of the plain honest truth of fighting for what I wanted. Even my need to write had been one never-ending battle against time, for working as a barmaid all day and taking the role of a mother in the evenings, with washing, ironing and every other household chore, meant my nights were not finished until somewhere around eleven o'clock. So the only time I could write was in the early hours of the morning. Until four o'clock, I would be scribbling away before falling exhausted into my bed. Only to be awakened by the screaming alarm clock at seven-thirty in time to wake the children ready for school.

Looking back at the years of my sleepless nights, my eyes burning with constant strain, I suppose these circumstances must have contributed to my fate.

And now today my sense of survival is even greater as I write in the frustrated torment of blindness.

CHAPTER FIFTEEN

After my third month in Rachel Dr Bright was delighted with my progress, in fact so pleased was she, she suggested I might, like Lucy, become a day patient, which meant I could go home each evening to sleep. Dr Bright's plan was that I should stay at my mother's house in Wanstead.

My sad daughter Sarah had taken it upon herself to come and visit me, and I found out Sarah was suffering from a bout of black depression. So great had been her fretting in my absence, her rapidly thinning body was completely covered in an ugly nerve-rash. It was clever Dr Bright's intent that fretting little Sarah and I could help each other, and the idea worked beautifully. Sarah and I snuggled up together in my mother's lovely old-fashioned feather bed, and happy Mum, surrounded by her daughter and grand-daughter's presence, would wake us each morning with two bone-china cups of tea. Sarah's spots disappeared and I put on one stone in weight.

In the warm privacy of our bed, our con-tented toes rested on hot soft rubber bottles, placed lovingly beneath the rose-pink flan-nelette sheets by Mother.

'Just think,' I would whisper to sleepy Sarah in the moon-striped darkness of our cosy room, 'you will never grow old for I will always remember your face as pretty as it is now.'

I was suspended in a world of never-ending youth and beauty. Never would I witness the sight of time with its merciless talent for placing unwanted wrinkles of age upon the faces of my friends and relatives. In my mind's eye no one would lose a tooth or hair for they would remain for ever young and beautiful. Even the fast hand of progress would not affect me one bit. No trees would disappear from my horizon in order to make way for the fast-growing jungles of grey, cold concrete. Children would stay children. No man would shrink and crawl with age, they would be for ever strong and upright, with their heads held high. My own hair would always remain the colour of a glossy black-bird's wing, for time was unable to interfere with my sightless memory of yesteryears.

Mother filled our bellies with large suet puddings and pies, fussing over us like we were poor hungry orphans. But alas, my aged stepfather George was each day more feeble and breathless, the pains in his wheezing chest were giving my tired mother many sleepless nights. Until one day the doctor called and immediately phoned for an ambulance, for my stepfather was in the first stage of pneumonia, fighting and gasping for life. I noticed my mother was picking Sarah up on her every movement. Mum was also becoming very nervous and forgetful.

Each time I showed my concern at her extreme tiredness, she would snap at me as she had done when I was a child. I knew she couldn't cope with the daily travelling to Walthamstow to visit my sick stepfather, then rushing home collecting her shopping on the way, and flying about her small kitchen hastily preparing the evening meal for Sarah and me. At night she would sit worrying about her husband's health, and would wearily climb the stairs to bed at three o'clock in the morning. Mother would then be up at six-thirty in order to prepare my injection, give me breakfast, and see me off on the eight o'clock ambulance.

I decided I must return back home to Jim, even though Dr Bright strongly opposed my wishes, warning me of the inevitable consequences. But no matter what she advised, I took no heed and assured Dr Bright that I would prove her wrong in respect of another mental collapse caused by my hostile home life. I knew in myself that I was once again strong and that I could cope with any obstacle put in my path.

I had already begun my book on Rachel with the help of an ingenious shutter-blind writing board, supplied by the blind welfare people. The fact that I had at last gained enough confidence to start writing once again convinced wary Dr Bright of my ability to maintain my mental health.

In any case, I would not be home for long, for the next month I would be in Devon amidst the loneliness of the blind. It had been said by Mr Curtis that my residential learning place would be for the spring period of three months.

I looked forward to the next stage, which held out the promise of new experiences, of learning more and more of people and places. For now, in the glowing mid-stream of life, I felt I could see more than I had ever seen before.

I stood, a woman of thirty-eight, full of innocent apprehension, like that of a help-less newborn infant, someone who had to be taught to walk upright and proud in the curious maze of general society and learn anew the ordinary ways of communication. And I would have to learn my alphabet of mystic mathematical Braille so I could with patience and perseverance solve the dark puzzle of reading and writing.

The birth of my new life would also mean re-education in eating manners, enabling me to sit with true inner dignity at the dinner table, even if it meant having to discard the common cutting-knife for an easy scooping spoon. And I would retain my independence through knowing the exact time of day, without having to impose on any other person for such simple information.

As I sit in the loneliness of my inner self, I hear the faint quadrophonic echoes of the downstairs television, and the blurry singing pub opposite my home. So great is my need to learn and be taught, I feel my forehead swelling and throbbing with the nauseating hunger for knowledge.

My fear of freedom is silently submerging into the calm sense of true belonging. I have at long last found a strange group of society to which I belong, and what grave difference does it make if my seeing has led me to the land of the lost, once mentally and now visually? For at least I have the kind inner warmth of a hand that rests in mine whenever I feel afraid, and the beautiful sensitive lips of a loving nutcase upon my damp cheeks whenever I weep for fond attention.

I, like many others, cannot exist without real love, and if the only way I can get the proper food for my soul is to struggle along the bitter-sweet path of the handicapped rejects of society, then who am I to question the ways of fate with all its weird and wonderful events and strange circumstances?